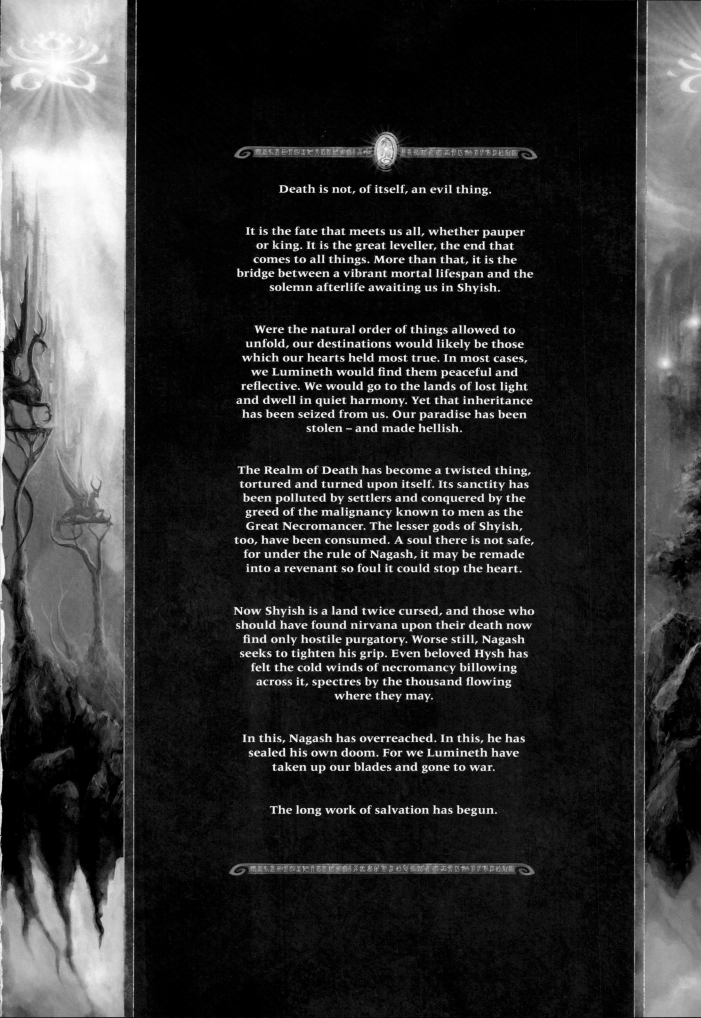

Death is not, of itself, an evil thing.

It is the fate that meets us all, whether pauper or king. It is the great leveller, the end that comes to all things. More than that, it is the bridge between a vibrant mortal lifespan and the solemn afterlife awaiting us in Shyish.

Were the natural order of things allowed to unfold, our destinations would likely be those which our hearts held most true. In most cases, we Lumineth would find them peaceful and reflective. We would go to the lands of lost light and dwell in quiet harmony. Yet that inheritance has been seized from us. Our paradise has been stolen – and made hellish.

The Realm of Death has become a twisted thing, tortured and turned upon itself. Its sanctity has been polluted by settlers and conquered by the greed of the malignancy known to men as the Great Necromancer. The lesser gods of Shyish, too, have been consumed. A soul there is not safe, for under the rule of Nagash, it may be remade into a revenant so foul it could stop the heart.

Now Shyish is a land twice cursed, and those who should have found nirvana upon their death now find only hostile purgatory. Worse still, Nagash seeks to tighten his grip. Even beloved Hysh has felt the cold winds of necromancy billowing across it, spectres by the thousand flowing where they may.

In this, Nagash has overreached. In this, he has sealed his own doom. For we Lumineth have taken up our blades and gone to war.

The long work of salvation has begun.

CONTENTS

PRODUCED BY THE WARHAMMER STUDIO
With thanks to The Faithful for their additional playtesting services

Warhammer Age of Sigmar – Broken Realms: Teclis © Copyright Games Workshop Limited 2020. Broken Realms, GW, Games Workshop, Warhammer, Warhammer Age of Sigmar, Battletome, Stormcast Eternals, and all associated logos, illustrations, images, names, creatures, races, vehicles, locations, weapons, characters, and the distinctive likenesses thereof, are either ® or TM, and/or © Games Workshop Limited, variably registered around the world. All Rights Reserved.

Games Workshop Ltd., Willow Road, Lenton, Nottingham, NG7 2WS, United Kingdom
games-workshop.com

DRAMATIS PERSONAE

The rise of the Lumineth, precipitated by Teclis' forays into the Mortal Realms, saw the aelves restore order across a hundred war-torn nations. They and their allies did not stand uncontested – indeed, amongst the cast of madmen, tyrants and kings that opposed them was the Great Necromancer himself.

GODS OF THE MORTAL REALMS

- **Teclis, Archmage of Hysh:** Twin god of the Realm of Light and master of magic.

- **Tyrion, the Lord of Lumination:** Twin god of the Realm of Light and bringer of deadly enlightenment.

- **Nagash, the Great Necromancer, Supreme Lord of the Undead:** Ruler of Shyish, self-styled God of Death, creator of the Shyish Nadir and bringer of the Necroquake.

- **Alarielle, the Everqueen:** Ruler of Ghyran, mother of the Sylvaneth and sworn enemy of Nurgle.

- **Malerion, the Shadow King:** Ruler of Ulgu, master of deception and embittered son of Morathi.

LUMINETH REALM-LORDS

- **Lyrior Uthralle, Lord Regent of Ymetrica:** Troubled but valorous second of Tyrion. A gifted master of warfare.

- **The Light of Eltharion, Champion of Teclis:** Warrior spirit of old without physical form, yet whose enchanted armour and blade lend him a matchless lethality.

- **The Weeping Veil:** Scinari Cathallar of Ymetrica and chief consul of the Teclian Vanguard invading Shyish's Ossiarch Empire.

- **Avalenor, the Stoneheart King:** Indomitable Spirit of the Mountain and aelementor of Avalenoria.

- **Ellania and Ellathor:** Scinari warsages and protégés of the aelven twin gods.

- **Sevireth, Lord of the Seventh Wind:** Spirit of the Wind and bringer of the Red Gale.

- **Harantio, the Galerider of Helon Coreward:** Legendary Hurakan Windmage and first of the Helon aelementiri.

MINIONS OF NAGASH

- **Arkhan the Black, Mortarch of Sacrament:** Ancient liche-sorcerer and right hand of the Great Necromancer.

- **Mannfred von Carstein, Mortarch of Night:** Ruthless strategist and last of the infamous von Carsteins.

- **Queen Neferata, Mortarch of Blood:** Ruler of Neferatia in the Prime Innerlands and mistress of a spy network that traverses the Mortal Realms.

- **Vokmortian, Master of the Bone-tithe:** Prime emissary of the Ossiarch Empire.

- **Horrek Venzai, Liege-Kavalos of Equuis Main:** Ossiarch master of the heavy cavalry assault.

- **Xaramos the Ossifector:** Master bone-sculptor of the Mortis Praetorians sent to besiege Ymetrica.

- **Archregent Gorstane Mortevell, the Bright Emperor:** Macabre leader of the Vertigon Flesh-eater Court.

- **Varshorn, King of Starfang Mont:** Lesser monarch of the Vertigon Court and would-be freedom fighter.

CHAMPIONS OF ORDER

- **Arcobalde Lazerne:** Senior member of the Collegiate Arcane in Hysh and leader of the Xintil War-magi.

- **Imoda Barrasdottr:** Perspicacious Kharadron admiral of Barak-Zilfin and nigh-obsessive cartographer.

SERVANTS OF THE DARK GODS

- **Horticulous Slimux, the Grand Cultivator:** Nurgle's first gardener and curmudgeonly master of the annexed Invidia.

- **Rotigus:** Great Unclean One and bringer of the Plaguefather's deluge.

- **Gortle Pulpskull:** Sloppity Bilepiper of the Invidian Plaguehost and under-appreciated jester of Horticulous Slimux's entourage.

- **Noddrack the Snitch:** Spoilpox Scrivener and avowed critic of Pulpskull's performances.

A moon, it is said, sees all under its light.

Can the same be said for the gods?

I, Celennar, know this. I always have. The Twin,
he has given me the words to speak of it.

Is it a blessing, or is it a curse?

Once, wherever my illumination shone, I saw the
truth – or a version of it. No more.

What lurks behind the masks of men?

Reality, once laid out before us like a scintillating
paradise, has been despoiled.

Can it be sanctified in time?

The weave and weft of the material realm is
ravaged, torn by the storms of anarchy and death.

Have they come to their senses too late?

There, beneath the shroud that the Dead One has
thrown over all the lands, is deep anger.

Is it the wrath of the realms?

But there is hope.
Enlightenment can yet save us all.

Even those who do not wish to be saved?

THE STORM OF GHEISTS

The city of Settler's Gain in Hysh was a place of high spires and soaring achievement, built upon the barren wilderness at the dawn of the Age of Sigmar. But even the favour of its Lumineth sponsors did not mean it was immune to the crippling effects of the Necroquake. Then, in its darkest hour, a true saviour appeared…

In the space of a single night, a jewel in Xintil's crown had transformed from a metropolis of glittering sanctity to a place of blackest terror.

Settler's Gain was under siege. Not from an army, nor a savage horde, but from a tide of living nightmares. The Nighthaunt hosts had emerged from the haze-shrouded horizon to charge straight for the city's outskirts, a howling, shrieking wave of ectoplasmic revenants that was proving nigh impossible to stop. On it came in a rush of distended skulls, tattered rags and grasping, grave-cold claws.

The alabaster perimeter wall of Settler's Gain provided scant defence. Even the warding sigils carved into every ten-metre stretch – under the express instructions of the Lumineth aelves who kept vigil over the city's construction – were little impediment. After the costly lessons that the Nighthaunt had learnt at Glymmsforge in Shyish, they knew well to prepare the advance. Many of the sigils had been compromised mere hours before the gheist attack by agents of Nagash who had infiltrated the city's outer sprawl. The locations of the damaged sigils had been conveyed by tattered raven messengers to the Knights of Shrouds leading the assault, and the Nighthaunt hosts attacked the city accordingly, pouring past the defensive fire of the Freeguilders manning the walls and simply passing through the compromised areas.

The warning chimes of invasion rang out in a great cacophony, light-flares bursting above the city limits to cast a fulsome glow in the dusky twilight of Hysh's night. Everywhere, warriors awoke from their slumber or meditation to strap on breastplate, draw blade and nock arrow. They formed up into ranks in the city streets in imitation of the Lumineth's own shining companies, shoulder to shoulder and shield to shield. When they saw the oncoming wall of shrieking ghosts, those who felt the icy tendrils of fear constrict around their hearts were swiftly slain, for their speartips and swords passed straight through the tortured spirits. Those who steeled themselves, who found courage in invoking Sigmar – or Teclis, come to that – struck true and watched the spirits dissipate into nothingness. But as more and more of the hideous creatures hurtled through the city's walls, soon even the most redoubtable company was beset on all sides.

Settler's Gain was one of the major metropolises of Sigmar's new order, and it would not be conquered easily. The Xintilian citizens of Settler's Gain had studied well under their Lumineth tutors, and the most scholarly of their number knew ways to banish gheist and daemon. Better yet, the Lumineth themselves were descending from the high spires. Pockets of resistance appeared all through the Simple Districts as the citizens gathered their defences around one learned in the arcane arts. The flashes of light that blazed into the undead hosts banished great swathes of chain-wrapped spectres.

Then came the Lumineth hosts themselves. First were the Dawnriders, aglow with lambent energy, who charged through the milling citizenry without so much as brushing against them. Speartips blazed with Hyshian energy moments before their cavalry charge hit home, ripping through each spectre to send the remnants shrieking back to the oubliettes of Shyish. Where the gheists rushed down alleys and boulevards towards the Vanari lines, searing arrows would shoot overhead to decimate their vanguard while Auralan Wardens shored up each route of escape with a wall of glowing spearpoints. These were no normal soldiers; they were warriors of Hysh, and their every weapon harnessed the power of aetherquartz to land a telling blow.

In the Quarter Harmonious, the battle mages of the Collegiate Arcane hurried out from their latest symposium and took to the field upon eldritch wagons of their own design. Hurricanums forced back the oncoming riot of spirits with barrages of Azyrite energy, lightning lashing out to dissipate outriding gheists. Arcobalde Lazerne, master of the city's mages, accompanied his pride and joy – the Luminark known as the *Beacon of Intellect* – into the fray. Its enchanted lens array sent beams of killing light searing into the thick of the Nighthaunt horde, burning dozens into nothing at a stroke.

Banishment after banishment took its toll, yet always there were more. The distant haze roiling upon the horizon at the beginning of the invasion proved to be no meteorological phenomenon but a wall of gheists borne upon the aftershock of the Shyish Necroquake, each howling for the souls of the living. The Nighthaunt swarm broke upon the city walls, no longer passing through but instead boiling over with the unstoppable momentum of a tsunami. Auralan Sentinels fired pinpoint shots into the morass of spirits, picking out their leaders and the bearers of balefully glowing relics. They slowed the invading host not at all.

It became painfully clear that there was no holding back the onrushing tide of Nighthaunt. They were driven by a rippling bow wave of death magic, yet this wave could not be broken, neither by chasm nor mountain nor castle wall. Worse still, they were striking the city on not one front but two. Though Lumineth reinforcements were descending from the high spires at the heart of the city, they could not mobilise quick enough to stem the flow of gheists, no more than a team of masons could stem the flow of a lake when the dam had already broken.

The careful training of the human populace gave them discipline enough to fight back for the first few hours, but as midnight came, their collective resolve began to waver. Black flowers of crippling terror blossomed in the hearts of all those who witnessed the Nighthaunt's onslaught. Elongated fangs sunk into pulse-pounding necks, while iron-hard talons ripped open ribcages as if they were made of straw. Leering death's head skulls pressed up against windows and arrow slits, the gheists laughing with maniacal glee as they simply drifted through the barriers and began the slaughter all over again.

Then came hope. It appeared not in the form of an aelf but in that of a giant, winged quadruped, regal and upright with a serene mask in place of its face: the lunasphinx Celennar, spirit of Hysh's true moon. A nimbus of moonlight surrounded the entity as it descended from the skies, its sphere of illumination spreading swiftly through the streets. Where its lambent energies touched one of the undead invaders, the gheist was pushed back, seared and discorporated like rags cast into a gale. In response to the being's arrival, a great hellish conveyance, borne aloft by nightmarish destriers, veered into the sky at full pace towards the newcomer, its wraithly carriage masters screaming in anger. The creature did not so much as twitch. Instead, it spoke a clear and singular word, a name with such power it could move mountains:

'TECLIS.'

For a split second, all light seemed to be sucked into a space above the sphinx-like creature's head. Then, bursting from nothingness like a star being suddenly born, Archmage Teclis appeared in his full majesty. Solar flares curled out from him, lashing through the streets. To the humans and aelves who initially recoiled in fear and confusion, their touch was as cool and refreshing as immersion in a moonlit lake. Not so for the Nighthaunt; screaming in agony, light poured from empty eye sockets and jaws opened unnaturally wide before the gheists were blasted apart into scattering spirit-ash.

A trio of undead knights careened through a nearby bell tower, trailing ethereal flame as they rode through the air straight for Teclis. With their blades raised, their hollow voices called out the name of the Great Necromancer, hoping to invoke his protection. A tiny smile appeared on the Mage God's thin lips, his eyes glowing bright as he reached into the depths of his knowledge of Shyish. A moment later, the wraith-riders transformed from tortured Nighthaunt into spirits untouched by Nagash's cruel spells, and then, as they approached the sphere of moonlight around Celennar, they became mortal riders and steeds once more. With cries of alarm and confusion, they plummeted one by one from the skies, crashing to their deaths in the streets below.

The Mage God raised his staff high, and the energy of Hysh streamed through him like light refracted through a prism. Burning lances of energy – some bright yellow, some scintillating blue, some pinkish-red – shot out from Teclis in all directions, each striking one of the Nighthaunt leaders in the streets below. In an instant, noose-wrapped murderers and looming hangmen were banished, screaming banshees were silenced forever and hourglass-bearing spectres shrank to pinpricks of darkness before disappearing entirely.

The people of Settler's Gain joined their voices in jubilation, the streets ringing with rapturous praise for the Mage God as Teclis rose high. 'The saviour has come,' they shouted. 'The day shall be won; we can drive back the night!' And with the speaking of those words, they became true.

The pall of despair that had settled over the city's defenders began to lift. Each new charge or lightning assault added to the feeling that the tide was turning, that the trespassing gheists would be nothing more than a fading nightmare come the full burn of day. In the Quarter Harmonious, the Luminarks and Hurricanums of the human wizards trundled down the Triumphal Boulevard to meet the shining companies of Lumineth coming the other way. United by their intimate knowledge of the city's streets and taking new hope from the glowing bursts of light that illuminated them, the aelves and humans gradually formed blockades and quarantines – and then, as they pressed their attack, killing fields. Only a scant few Nighthaunt leaders escaped banishment, riding hard into the distance to bring word to their masters of the disaster. Behind them, they left the rough masses of their invading hordes, forsaken twice over and left to their own fate in the face of the vengeful Xintilian hosts.

It took the entire night and the day after that to purge the city of the curse that had befallen it. Many thousands lay dead in the streets when the butcher's bill was counted, and hundreds of those would have no peace in death: their features were contorted into rictuses of terror or anguish, and their souls were already forfeit, borne away on the ebb tide of the Necroquake that had caused their demise. They were buried with full honours at Teclis' demand, and their names were inscribed upon the great Pillar of Martyrs. Yet for all the damage done to Settler's Gain in those first few terrible hours, the city had emerged all the stronger for it. Word had spread that even should the darkest army of undeath make its assault, the citizens of Hysh could hurl back the darkness. It was a fine tale indeed – and, for a while at least, it endured.

The Harrow-Knight crawled up the ninety-ninth stair of Nagashizzar, every iota of his being shivering with the effort. Even to draw the gaze of the master was to risk an eternity of torture.

Around the God of Undeath were ranged antique mirrors of shadeglass. Though two were empty, three bore the reflections of Nagash's foremost Mortarchs. Around them, the air pulsed with magical potential, almost audible despite the dirges of the spirits far below.

Then, from atop his godly throne, the monstrous figure spoke. 'KNIGHT OF REGRET, DELIVER THY TRUTH.'

'Great one,' managed the Harrow-Knight, his voice a hollow rasp. 'A god of light, at Xintil. He had a masked beast. It glowed like the moon.'

'IT **WAS** THE MOON. ITS MASTER IS NAMED TECLIS.'

The Harrow-Knight was not fool enough to reply. He merely grovelled, fleshless face pressed against the stone of Nagash's royal dais.

'TELL ME OF HIS BANISHMENTS,' said the Great Necromancer.

'I'll tell you myself,' said a cultured voice.

The Harrow-Knight saw a mote of light above him, which began to unfold like a paper sculpture of fractal complexity into the form of a tall, robed figure that shone with brilliant luminosity. The Mage God. It hurt to look upon him.

'TECLIS OF ULTHUAN,' said Nagash, his voice like the grinding of glaciers. 'YOUR INTRUSION WILL NOT GO UNPUNISHED.'

'I could say the same of yours,' said Teclis. 'You have rather overstepped your bounds of late.'

'WHEREVER THERE IS DEATH, I LAY MY CLAIM. DO YOU THINK YOURSELF IMMUNE, AELFLING?'

'No,' said Teclis, shaking his head slowly. 'Though it will not be you who ends me, Nehekharan. Celennar has assured me of that.'

'BE NOT SO SURE. THE MOON REFLECTS THE TRUTH, BUT IN DOING SO, IT DISTORTS IT. YOUR EMPIRE WILL FALL, AND YOUR SPIRES WILL LIE IN THE DIRT ONCE MORE.'

The Harrow-Knight felt the aelven god scan the room like a searchlight, taking in the shadeglass mirrors one by one. The Mortarchs reflected within recoiled as his gaze passed across them.

'If that is true, it will not be you who topples it,' said Teclis. 'I give you one last chance, Great Nagash. Withdraw your influence from Hysh, or your own necrotopian empire will die in the cradle.'

There was a sudden cessation of background noise. The Harrow-Knight looked down at the Ossiarch warriors that had been marching in great columns at the base of the throne. They were stock still, and all were staring at the astral image of Teclis hovering before Nagash.

'WE SHALL SEE,' said Nagash, the air around him crackling with hoarfrost as his ire cooled to a lethal chill. 'WE SHALL SEE.'

The Great Necromancer took up the staff Alakanash and thrust it forwards. In that moment, the luminous apparition was gone, and the throne room darkened once more.

'YOU HAVE YOUR ORDERS, MORTARCHS,' said Nagash, turning back to the antique mirrors. 'COLLAPSE THE GATES TO SHYISH. LET LOOSE THE PULL OF THE NADIR TO THOSE REALMS THAT THINK THEMSELVES SAFE.' He leaned forwards, eye sockets blazing. 'AND MAKE SURE THAT HYSH SUFFERS THE MOST.'

Nagash turned from the mirrors, one hand summoning a cloud of spirits that bore him up and out of the chamber with great reverence.

Had he still breath to hold, the Harrow-Knight would have exhaled a great sigh of relief. Instead, he let himself fade into ephemeral mist and vanished from Nagashizzar without a word.

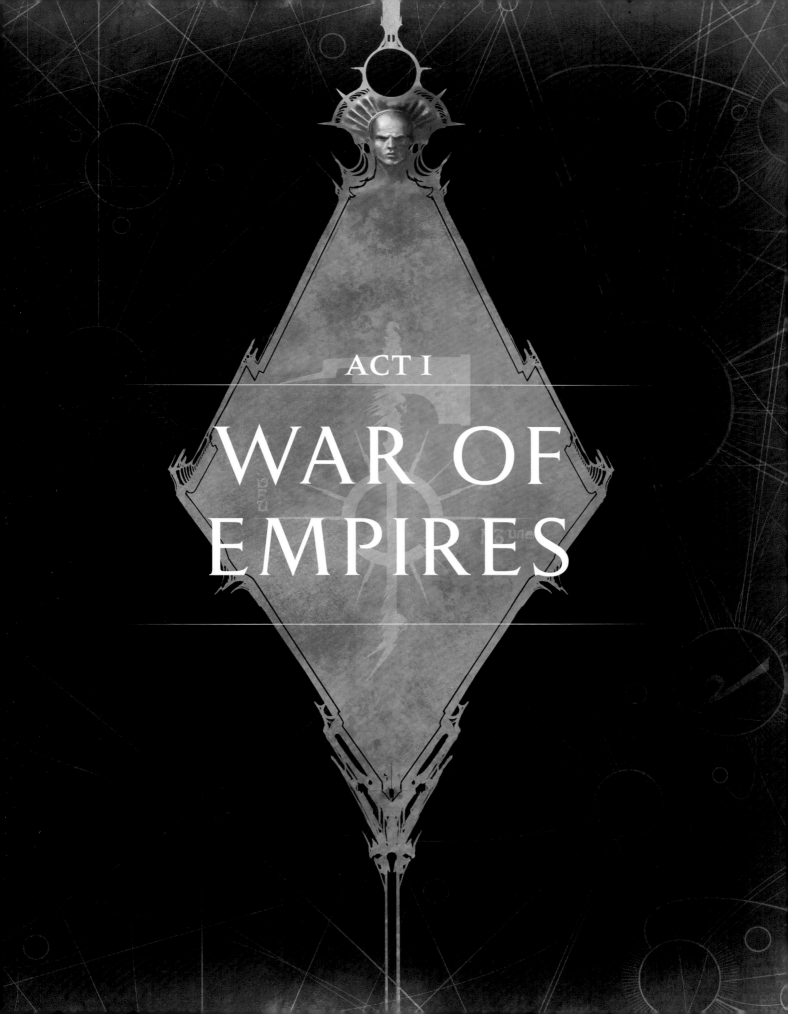

ACT I

WAR OF EMPIRES

THE FIRST SPEARING

The first of the Lumineth hosts to go forth into the realms were known as the Teclian Vanguard, for the Mage God himself masterminded their assault. Their target was the grouping of Shyishan underworlds known as the Ossiarch Empire.

To invade the heartlands of Nagash's necrotopia was to begin a war across reality – a war between life and death itself. Teclis did not shrink from it. The cosmos, so badly destabilised by the Age of Chaos and shaken to its foundations by the Necroquake, was in dire need of healing. It was that healing that Teclis sought to provide – whether the other people of the realms wished it or not.

The Lumineth made their first forays into Shyish via a long-sealed realmgate in the Magthar Mountains of Hallost. All but completely obscured by the looming peaks, it was unknown even to the spectral heroes who haunted the region. The Lumineth crossed the Nihilat Reach, borne atop floating rocks that their Alarith Stonemages had pressed into their service, and launched a devastating assault on the Mortis Praetorians of the Necrarch Coast, all before word had reached Katakros of their presence in the Realm of Death.

Making their way through the gap in the Nightfire Spine mountains before they could be intercepted by Katakros' legions, the Lumineth traversed the Great Plains of Praetoris and advanced upon the trio of towering fortress-statues known as the Triptych. Were it not for Katakros being engaged in a war of wits with Archaon the Everchosen, they would soon have been waylaid. Instead, within a week of their arrival in Shyish, the Teclian Vanguard had made it to the heart of the Ossiarch Empire, and they stood poised to strike.

WARRING NATIONS
The Ossiarch Empire has already begun expanding across the neighbouring Prime Innerlands at Katakros' behest.

> **KEY**
> ✳ *Necropolis-level stronghold*
> ▼ *Fortress-level stronghold*
> — *Geomantic pathway*

← TO THE PRIME INNERLANDS

NEROZZAR
An immense citadel of bone overlooks the Pentaghul River and the slender bridge that crosses it.

CRIPPLECOAST · JHYND · WEST OCCULUS · EAST OCCULUS · LYRIA · INCISUM · INCISTUS · THE TARKAN CONQUEST · ENDLESS BONEYARD · NECROPOLIS OF CARTOCH · MYRMID · SATYR'S END · CHORA · MAGTHAR MOUNTAINS · HALLOST · LAND OF DEAD HEROES · DRIFTWOOD BEACHES · NIHILAT REACH · NECRARCH COAST · THE RED PLAINS · NYAZZAR · THE BLACK NIHIL · SKELT · HARMON · CAPE GHOUL · CORDIAZA · MORTHAVEN · THE SKULL ISLES · ODT · MOSS SPIKE · BOTTLENECK COAST · QUINTUS SPINE · NECROS · THRICE-CURSED ISLANDS · SPURIA · ELEGIAC PE[...] · CADA[...] · GOTHIZZAR · ENDGATE · XALACAR · HAG'S CLAW · COR MORTIFUS · THE SKAVEN DROWNINGS · THETZAR TI · LAND OF LIVING BONE · HAIKAZ · OSSIA[...] · PHALANG[...] ISLES · UR-SKUL DELTA · TOVA HIN · EAST OSSIAN SEA

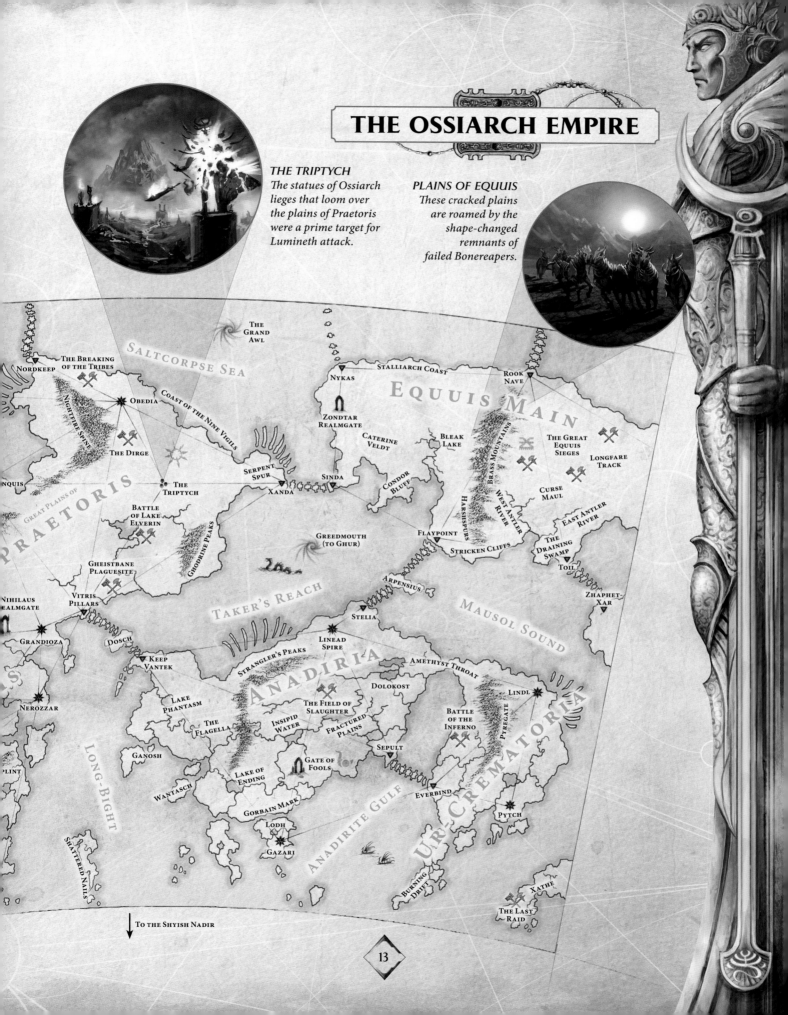

THE OSSIARCH EMPIRE

THE TRIPTYCH
The statues of Ossiarch lieges that loom over the plains of Praetoris were a prime target for Lumineth attack.

PLAINS OF EQUUIS
These cracked plains are roamed by the shape-changed remnants of failed Bonereapers.

THE GRAND AWL

SALTCORPSE SEA

STALLIARCH COAST

EQUUIS MAIN

NORDKEEP

THE BREAKING OF THE TRIBES

NYKAS

ROOK NAVE

OBEDIA

COAST OF THE NINE VIGILS

ZONDTAR REALMGATE

NIGHTFIRE SPINE

THE DIRGE

CATERINE VELDT

BLEAK LAKE

BRASS MOUNTAINS

THE GREAT EQUUIS SIEGES

LONGFARE TRACK

NQUIS

SERPENT SPUR

SINDA

CONDOR BLUFF

CURSE MAUL

THE TRIPTYCH

XANDA

WEST ANTLER RIVER

EAST ANTLER RIVER

GREAT PLAINS OF PRAETORIS

BATTLE OF LAKE ELVERIN

GHODRINE PEAKS

GREEDMOUTH (to Ghur)

FLAYPOINT

HARSHSPURS

THE DRAINING SWAMP

GHEISTBANE PLAGUESITE

STRICKEN CLIFFS

TOIL

ARPENSIUS

NIHILAUS REALMGATE

VITRIS PILLARS

TAKER'S REACH

STELIA

MAUSOL SOUND

ZHAPHET-XAR

GRANDIOZA

DOSCH

LINEAD SPIRE

KEEP VANTEK

STRANGLER'S PEAKS

ANADIRIA

AMETHYST THROAT

DOLOKOST

LINDL

NEROZZAR

LAKE PHANTASM

THE FIELD OF SLAUGHTER

BATTLE OF THE INFERNO

PYREGATE

THE FLAGELLA

INSIPID WATER

FRACTURED PLAINS

GANOSH

LONG-BIGHT

LAKE OF ENDING

GATE OF FOOLS

SEPULT

EVERBIND

UR-CREMATORIA

WANTASCH

GORBAIN MARK

ANADIRITE GULF

PYTCH

LODH

GAZARI

SHATTERED NAILS

BURNING DRIFT

XATHE

THE LAST RAID

↓ To the Shyish Nadir

PLINT

13

A STATEMENT OF INTENT

The Lumineth of the Teclian Vanguard realised full well that they could not hope to invade the heartlands of the Ossiarch Empire without encountering untenable resistance. But their goal was not conquest in the traditional manner – Teclis' plan had far more to do with symbolic victory than territorial gains.

Deep in the snow-shrouded Magthar Mountains, a small point of light glowed bright above a glassy lake, still liquid despite the icy temperatures. The lake was hidden from the paths of men and ghosts, not only by bluffs and steep escarpments but also by powerful illusions woven millennia ago. The light above the lake turned from a glimmer to a will-o'-the-wisp, then something akin to ball lightning. Animals and birds fled in all directions; only the glow-moths stayed to dance around it, too curious and small-minded to sense the danger. Then, with a swift pulse of energy, the globe of light exploded, its essence sucked down into the still lake beneath.

A rank of steel triangles broke the surface, then another. Speartips. Out from the lake marched a dozen Auralan Wardens, their pikes held high. Water drizzled from their immaculate uniforms as they wordlessly established a perimeter around the lake's edge, but they paid it no mind even as it turned to ice upon them in the freezing cold – their focus was absolute. Next to appear from the glowing lake were sharp-eyed archers, equally unfazed by the aquatic vector of their arrival. They too took up position, climbing high onto the rocks to spy out any potential routes from which a foe could attack. Within minutes, an entire Auralan legion had assembled, the area claimed by Lumineth whose breath frosted in the air.

With the area secure, one of the Vanari leaders summoned an orb of light in between his fingers and sent it into the pool as if throwing a single pebble. The water did not ripple, but its glow steadily increased to envelop the lake and its environs in a dome of light. Within this hemisphere, the temperature rose until the snow began to melt, revealing lush vegetation that turned its flowers to the sky.

Only then did the remainder of the Teclian Vanguard emerge in great splendour from the lake. Last to surface was the Archmage himself, rising in glory amidst streams of golden, glimmering water with his lunasphinx companion at his side. He spoke at length, not only to the assembled aelves but to the peaks themselves. The shoulders of the mountains cracked, menhirs and great shelves of rock sloughing away to hover as rocky platforms at Teclis' side. The Lumineth Realm-lords had come to Shyish.

THE BLOW DESCENDS

The assault of the Lumineth upon the Ossiarch Empire was swift. Borne through the skies upon the rocky platforms harnessed by the realm magic of Teclis and his Alarith Stonemages – all masters in the art of geomancy and, hence, the manipulation of floating metaliths – they glided straight over the walled cities and bone-braced roads that Nagash's favoured had put so much effort into constructing. Where the catapults and artillery pieces mounted upon those walls sent projectiles arcing up towards them, flashing beams of light intercepted the missiles with pinpoint accuracy, blasting apart not only physical ammunition of stele and stone-hard skull but also the howling gheist-stuff that would otherwise have taken a fiendish toll on the aelven warriors.

The power of the Ossiarchs was not without its limits even in their own territory, for though they marched more swiftly and tirelessly than any mortal army, they could not keep pace with the Lumineth, borne as they were upon eerily floating shelves of stone. Wherever the land was rendered uninhabitable by the Necroquake, Teclis and his mages would enact a great rite to seal the area with a massive Lumineth rune, for the magic of the aelves could, should the right sigils be chosen, undo the taint of Shyishan magic as well as the corruption of Chaos. This alone was a great insult to the Ossiarchs, for it was their empire that Teclis was binding at whim. The destination of the Teclian Vanguard had been chosen for much the same reason – to make a statement, rather than a nationwide conquest. The aelves were to strike not at the walls or outskirts of Katakros' domain; they would attack one of its spiritual keystones.

Teclis had decided against the invasion of Gothizzar, the great fortress that Katakros called his own, for even he and his Lumineth would not make so foolish a mistake as to challenge the primary stronghold of the Ossian Mortarch. Instead, they made haste across the Great Plains of Praetoris to the trio of statue-topped fortresses collectively known as the Triptych.

The Triptych was considered one of the foremost wonders of Shyish. No mere landmark, it was a nexus of magical ways protected by three fortresses of smooth bone. Atop each of these was a colossal statue of one of the Ossiarch generals who had

distinguished themselves in the defence of Praetoris against the scourge of Chaos. The tallest and most impressive was that of Katakros himself. It was this site that Teclis intended to strike – and strike hard. Not only was it a vital waypoint between Praetoris and Equuis, but the toppling of such a monument to Katakros' vanity would be a symbolic act that would resonate throughout Shyish. In felling it, he would show the Ossiarchs to be fallible and far from unbeatable as a military force.

The initial attack was made not upon the plains – as the extensive Ossiarch garrison would have preferred it – but from the skies. With the floating metaliths still bearing them aloft, the Lumineth had an advantage they were loath to relinquish. Vanari archers rained volleys upon the Ossiarch hordes massing on the plains below, each glowing sunmetal arrowhead sending a bone warrior pitching into the dirt. The Bonereapers sent up winged Morghasts to intercept the flying islands, but as they neared, the Lumineth concentrated their magical offensive on those macabre angels of death. Even as Windmage and Cathallar tore the bone constructs from the skies, Calligrave rune-mages burned a giant icon of sanctity into the ground below. The enemy's Mortisan leaders were chanting long and loud, their sonorous

rites resounding in the air, but short of allowing the slain Ossiarch soldiery to rise once more, they were levelling little counter-magic in response.

Then the great statue of Katakros twisted with a groaning, protesting creak, swinging its colossal glaive of nullstone to smash into one of the floating metaliths and shatter it along its length. In that instant, the weapon's field of null energy unbound the geomantic magic holding the Magthari shelf aloft; the Lumineth aboard the falling metalith reeled and toppled to tumble, flailing, through the air. Celennar swooped, extending a wing, and caught them on a slanting plane of shimmering moonlight before lowering them gently to the plains below. Now the other two statues of the Triptych were coming to life, moving stiffly to bring their giant blades down and shatter the islands that had been used to transport the Lumineth's armies. The aelves aboard these metaliths were swift – most put themselves out of harm's way before the blades could crush them – but the rocks were as ponderous as the mountains and could not evade in time. One by one, they were smote heavily by the statues' polearms. One by one, they came crashing down to the plains below amidst an avalanche of debris. The Lumineth offensive had been brought to a sudden halt.

THE SPEARTIP BLUNTED

The Lumineth vanguard had taken an impressive toll on the Ossiarchs, but their assault had slowed. For though Katakros could not protect every square mile of the landscape, he had planned its defences for centuries. Teclis and his shining hosts were soon locked in a pitched battle against a foe like no other.

The Lumineth assault had been literally brought down by the immense feat of mortisanry that gave life to the Triptych statues. As giant hunks of mountain smashed into the ground, hundreds of Lumineth vaulted and leapt to safety – and not all of them found it. The massive, monolithic slabs of rock cleaved from the Magthar peaks gouged huge furrows in the plains before coming to a halt, sending many of those Lumineth still atop them falling toward the unforgiving earth until Teclis, an island of serenity amidst the toppling metaliths, reached out with a net of light to catch them and convey them to safety. He could not save them all, however. Aelves lay broken all around, their white robes stained red.

The Lumineth were still desperately trying to marshal some cohesion in their ranks when the first of the Mortek Guard were upon them. The Ossiarchs had marched slowly at first, the Vanari having considered them all but irrelevant as they picked out their leaders from their ranks. But their slow, methodical dispersal had put the lie to their true speed when under attack. Moving in quickstep, they closed on those aelves still stunned by the crash of their Alarith-guided metaliths, and they began to kill.

The aelves who had ridden out the assault remained atop the dark rocks upon which they had gained the battlefield scant minutes before. In these fallen platforms, they saw ready-made defensive positions – although out of action, they were still high ground, and they had sheer slopes that even an undead soldier would find difficult to traverse. In haste, the stony slabs were made into bastions. The Vanari took the fore once more, spearmen manning the cliff-like escarpments as archers fired into the fray.

Battle was joined across a dozen fronts, on the metaphysical level as well as the material. Teclis raised an eyebrow in surprise as the baleful energies of death magic assailed him from all sides and winged constructs converged upon him. Though those Ossiarch spellcasters who dared to match themselves against the Mage God paled in comparison to his mastery, they were numerous, and they were well coordinated in the way only those mind-linked to one another can be. He found himself having to focus on a dozen arcane duels simultaneously as Celennar tore into the Morghasts sent to assassinate him. Gradually, he gained the upper hand, his spells burning out one member of the Mortisan priesthood after another.

The armies of the Teclian Vanguard were independent and well drilled, their leaders more than capable of securing victory even without Teclis' help. Already sharp orders were ringing out across the battlefield, the commands of Realm-lord and Bonereaper tacticians set against one another in an ever-evolving contest of wits before the tempest of violence broke in earnest. The Ossiarch phalanxes approaching the largest of the Lumineth's stone bastions were once more bombarded with arrows as the Auralan Sentinels took their shots. This time, the Bonereapers were not so easily stymied. The Mortek Guard sallying forth from the Triptych fortresses raised their thick shields to cover their heads and torsos whilst simply ignoring those arrowheads that struck their limbs.

As the Ossiarchs neared the aelves, those in the middle of each phalanx brought their shields overhead and locked them together, while those on the edges made shieldwalls around the perimeter. These defensive formations were proof against even the marksmen of the Auralan Sentinel formations. Where the Mortek Guard gained the cliff face of the imposing metalith, they did not begin to climb – as the Lumineth had expected them to – but locked themselves in place, shields still held facing upwards to deflect the hail of projectiles launched from above. More and more Mortek Guard moved up to join them, for shielded as they were, even the searing bolts of light sent by the Scinari could do little more than scorch the bulwark of alchemically strengthened bone.

The Mortisans who approached the massing Ossiarch infantry chanted in their ancient, guttural tongue, whereupon the soldiers' shields – and even their bodies – melded together until they formed a living scaffold that extended up the cliff face. Warrior by warrior, the framework grew, extending higher up the cliff with every passing minute.

Then the hindmost Mortek Guard came in close, their formations larger and more impressive than those that had come before. In unison they moved their shields aside – and the reason suddenly became clear. Bursting out from beneath the shield canopy came groups of Necropolis Stalkers; having crawled on all six limbs beneath the shields of the Mortek Guard, they had remained hidden from the Lumineth who rained shots from above. Now they charged with incredible alacrity, scaling the Mortek scaffold and leaping the last dozen metres to catch the cliff edge with huge, bony claws. Grinning visages were shot point-blank by the Auralan Sentinels, but the Necropolis Stalkers simply rotated their heads until another of their four faces grimaced in its place, then hauled themselves over the edge and set about cutting down their aelven adversaries with sharp, chopping arcs of their spirit blades.

The Auralan Wardens were quick to respond, thrusting their pikes over the shoulders of their compatriots to force the grotesque Bonereaper constructs back. However, the simple fact was that the aelves had not the strength to repel them. At a command from the High Wardens, the Lumineth channelled the energy of their aetherquartz reserves; their speartips glowed bright and the air filled with the stench of cooking bone as they thrust them deep into the breastbones and armoured limbs of the Necropolis Stalkers. But this was not enough. The Ossiarch monstrosities slashed left and right with their many arms, cutting through the aelves' spear shafts as if they were no more than birch sticks. A clear note of retreat rang out, and the Vanari gave way, half covering the others as they dragged their fallen kin from the lip of the cliff.

Then came the Alarith Stoneguard, their tall, horned helms glinting in the light. The front-line troops of the Vanari flowed back through their ranks as the cloaked warriors moved in to take their place. They strove to keep their expressions neutral, for it is the aelementiri way to fight with a clear mind untainted by emotion, but given that they had just watched their kinsmen be carved apart by Ossiarch blades, this was no mean feat. Here was the face of death, but they were determined not to flinch from it.

ARCHMAGE TECLIS

Teclis has left an indelible mark on the histories of the aelves, humans and, of late, the Mortal Realms themselves. He is the father of magic in the enlightened nations, the conjurer of new races and the agent of ascension for the entire Lumineth civilisation. Yet much like his twin brother Tyrion, it is in his nature to destroy as well as to create.

In his first life, Teclis was born a twin, growing up in a peaceful province of ancient Ulthuan. He nearly died in infancy, for he was born runtish and slight. Even in adulthood, he had to resort to special restorative potions – and later the blessing of the moon goddess Lileath – to sustain him in times of strain. That distant time has become another life, another reality, and only a few besides Teclis and Tyrion even remember it. For in the Mortal Realms, the aelf lord has been reborn a god of light. He is brilliant of mind and radiant with power, hailed more than once as the saviour of the aelves. The dark truth is that he has also caused much of their demise.

A descendant of the doomed line of Aenarion, Teclis has always had a shadow upon him. Where Tyrion was fair and strong, Teclis was dark, gaunt

and sinister. Where his brother took the mastery of war as his own, Teclis instead sought expertise in the arcane arts. Since those early years, his boundless curiosity and natural proficiency saw him rise to become the pre-eminent mage of ancient Ulthuan, then fall into disaster at the ending of the World-that-Was. It was Teclis who unravelled the Great Vortex – a vast maelstrom that kept the magic of the world from reaching critical mass – and, in doing so, released the Winds of Magic from their bondage. He did so hoping that they would empower a pantheon-to-be, drawn to a set of eight chosen heroes who together would defeat Chaos. In a way, the great gamble worked: immense power was funnelled into those who most exemplified the natures of the various Winds. It was Tyrion who absorbed the Wind of Hysh after succumbing to the dark curse of Aenarion; though the Hyshian energy resurrected him, he has yet to escape the shadow of his bloodline.

The limitations of the aelven twins contributed to the destruction of the World Before Time when its defenders failed to hold back the final cataclysm. As the forces of Chaos pressed in, the curse of Aenarion's line – thought by many to have left Tyrion untouched – manifested as a killing rage. It was Teclis who saved his brother from utter damnation and gave him a chance to rise like a phoenix from the flames of the world's destruction. His twin brother was bound to him in spirit as well as body, and Teclis likewise took into himself the radiant essence of Hysh's power. While the vast majority of aelves were consumed by their nemesis Slaanesh, Tyrion and Teclis were reincarnated as gods.

Sigmar the God-King, while roaming in glimmering Hysh, found the two aelven deities in a nimbus of light. He was overjoyed to meet such spiritual comrades in a strange and foreign reality. They gained surety and focus from the bonds they shared, and for a time they were stalwart allies, with a common foe in Chaos and the scars of long wars fought against it. He has worked tirelessly against the dark powers over the millennia, striving for more and more influence to better oppose them on all fronts. He works marvels with words and tutelage whenever he can, spells when diplomacy is found wanting, and even with a blade – the Sword of Teclis, an ancient relic empowered by celestial Azyrite energies – when all else fails.

Teclis knows more of the secret ways of the realms than any other living creature save the slann, for he walked the Paths of the Old Ones as a mortal, and can astrally project across the cosmos with but a single hour of meditation. It is he that constructed the Tower of Prios in Xintil, a citadel of aetherquartz built in the likeness of the White Tower of Hoeth, where Teclis himself studied the magical arts. Were it not for that uncanny spire's exorcising radiance and precise geomantic location, the force of Nagash's Necroquake would have taken a far greater toll on Hysh.

Teclis has always been fascinated by the ranks of humanity, for though they are easily corrupted and pale in terms of intellect, they are endlessly adaptable. It was because of this potential that Teclis taught the most learned men of Sigmar's homeland some of the secrets of the arcane, which led to the creation of the Colleges of Magic. It was a feat of tutelage he was to replicate during the Age of Myth. Without Teclis' aid, there would be no Great

Nation of Xintil, no centres of Teclian learning such as Settler's Gain. Yet the alliance between Teclis and Sigmar has not always been smooth. Sigmar's bombastic and direct approach to the war against Chaos rankles greatly with both Tyrion and Teclis, who cannot help but see in him the bearded, roaring barbarian of the World-that-Was. When Teclis gifted Sigmar with the mighty Enlightenment Engines, intended to raise the intellect and arcane ability of all humans who dwelt near them, the God-King used them instead to excise dangerous knowledge from the minds of his people. In this, he showed a lack of vision that estranged Teclis for many years. The twins drifted away from the Pantheon of Order, instead looking to the salvation of their own race.

In their wanderings, they encountered their opposite numbers in the form of Morathi and Malerion, and a pact had been made. Together, the four godly presences wove the tapestries of magic to entrap their nemesis, Slaanesh, within the twilight realm known as the Hidden Gloaming. Over time, they extracted hundreds of aelven souls from their torturous existences within the Dark Prince's swollen gut. They were scarred by their ordeal, regardless of the form they took upon reincarnation. The Cythai, first to be freed, had withered souls and were prone to fits of excessive emotion. So shocked was Teclis that he resolved to extinguish them and start over with a clean slate. Were it not for Tyrion's plea for mercy, the Cythai would not have escaped their creator's wrath. As it was, they fled to the deepest, darkest places to hide from their persecutors – first amongst them Slaanesh, but also the Archmage Teclis – and in doing so, they became the Idoneth.

Many other experiments of magical salvation followed that of the Cythai, but it was the Lumineth that were to become Teclis' greatest creation. Unblemished and possessed of an abundance of talent, they were the true inheritors of Hysh's brilliance. For long centuries, they thrived, spreading their civilisation across the Great Nations of Hysh and raising their spires ever higher. Teclis taught them the ways of enlightenment, and they strove to climb to the lofty heights he had pioneered. In doing so, they lost touch with the realm that had lent them its grace, and developed a deadly solipsism that stains their souls to this day. Harmless rivalries led to hubristic ambition, resentment, then the horrendous civil wars of the Ocari Dara. This time, Teclis worked to save his people rather than to condemn them. He sought the wisdom of the entity Celennar, the spirit of Hysh's true moon. In pioneering a symbiosis between aelf and realm entity, he set in motion the Reinvention, allowing his race to become the Realm-lords of today.

RIDE OF THE VANARI

The Lumineth's improvised tactic of landing their metalith islands close to the Triptych fortresses led to a clash of strongholds that were almost within arrow's reach. A complex interplay of siege and counter-siege began, with each side vying for a decisive advantage – until a dramatic gamble ripped the stalemate open.

The Alarith flowed forward to replace the Vanari on the cliff edge, their magnificent helms glinting in the wan Shyishan light. Their spotless ochre robes were a stark contrast to the gore-spattered whites of those they relieved, but the newcomers too were soon smeared with dust, blood and flinders of bone. At first, the Stoneguard parried the blades of the towering Ossiarch war constructs with cold, machine-like efficiency, deflecting the foe's razored swords with the heads of their hammers and blocking their descending blows with the hafts. The Stonemages behind them chanted the songs of the mountains they called home, and as they took up the chant, their skin turned grey, hardening until they were as tough as stone. When the bone-sculpted giants brought their blades down upon their enemies, they rebounded without causing harm as often as they landed a telling blow.

With a series of macabre clicks, the Stalkers pivoted their heads upon their necks, going from chattering, grinning rictus to sombre death mask. Likewise, their attack patterns changed, switching from the lateral strikes of a sabre fighter to the pinpoint thrusts of a master duellist. Like rapiers, their swords lanced in with such force behind them that, this time, they punctured the Alarith's guard, their spirit blades bursting out of the backs of those they struck.

Yet for every blow the Ossiarchs landed upon the Alarith, a hammer blow was levelled in return. With the Necropolis Stalkers prioritising pinpoint offence, they inadvertently allowed the long-hafted hammers of their foes to strike hard at their carapaces of bone. However, such was the care and skill with which the Stalkers had been crafted that they were merely knocked back by the blows, not shattered. Then the second rank of Alarith warriors came into the fray, wielding their diamondpick hammers in such a way that the shining obelisk-like protrusions were driven point first into the Stalkers' bony forms. These were weapons devised to crack invictunite, and they penetrated the sternums and thoraxes of the Ossiarch constructs with a series of loud cracks.

Harder and harder came the Alarith offensive, each determined step – won at a high cost in Lumineth lives – pushing their foes back. The sheer tectonic force of their advance channelled the power of

their mountain aelementors, and inch by gruelling inch, the Necropolis Stalkers were forced to the very lip of the cliff. With one final push, the Alarith Stoneguard brought their hammers around in wide, swinging arcs and smashed the Ossiarch constructs clean off the edge of the escarpment, sending them flailing to shatter into dozens of pieces on the rock-strewn plains below.

As the Alarith of the largest Magthari bastion fought to hold their cliff edge, the Vanari of the smallest of the two found themselves fighting hard against the Mortek Guard of Fortress Tzantari. The rocky metalith had landed in such a way that it formed a jutting diagonal shelf, high on one side and low on the other – low enough that the Tzantari battalions could simply march up the sharp incline to attack the Lumineth echelons, who were still redressing their ranks after the staggering force of their crash-landing. The Bonereapers were approaching far faster than the aelves had anticipated and took swathes of ground, intending to grind the Lumineth off the rocky cliff of their own strongpoint. The Auralan troops, for their part, formed up shoulder to shoulder in the signature fighting style of the shining companies, for with such a great concentration of aetherquartz in one place, those born of the darkness would be forced to avert their gaze. To an Ossiarch Bonereaper, discomfort is meaningless, and the Mortek advanced without slowing. Yet the Lumineth had gained a slight ridge on the rocky cliff, and their true intent was not to blind – but to obscure.

As one, the Lumineth spearmen parted, filing back amongst each other so that they stood in widely spaced columns rather than tightly packed ranks. In a burst of brilliance, the Dawnriders they had hidden from sight came hurtling down the slender avenues left in the Vanari formation, riding in column only to fan out into a broad front as they left their Warden comrades behind. Leading by example, Lyrior Uthralle, Lord Regent of Ymetrica, gave a clarion war shout. His riders joined their voices with his in fierce elation; for them, this was the moment of truth.

The Mortek Guard adopted an aegis formation with instinctive speed, locking together their shields with the distinctive clack of bone on bone. Against a conventional cavalry charge, they might have held the line. Against lesser beasts of war, the unnatural energies resonating from the Ossiarchs may have turned the riding beasts aside at the last minute. But the Dawnriders were specialists in attacking infantry, and their noble steeds did not shrink from the deathly scions of Nagash.

In the moment before impact, bright shafts of luminescent magic beamed out from the aetherquartz gems on the Dawnriders' helms and armour, sizzling through the heavy air to find the eye sockets of the Ossiarchs set for the charge. The Steedmaster champions of the Dawnrider Lance gave a curt command, and in response, the riders gave the signal for their steeds to leap high. No human-trained horses would have made the jump, but these were Xintilian stallions, and they were brave indeed.

The Ossiarch Bonereapers jabbed out their spears, intending to impale their foes' fine white horses as they sailed overhead, but the Dawnriders were ready for them. Down swept their sunmetal lances, turning spears aside as a fencer parries thrusting blades. With the way cleared, the wedge drove home, pounding hooves crushing the Ossiarchs set to repel them as the sheer weight of the muscular beasts sent their foes staggering into the dirt. The Dawnrider charge shattered the ranks behind the shieldwall without being slowed by its forward elements. At the heart of the charge was Illustraine Vetare himself, whose golden blade had taken the head of the formation's Hekatos with a low sweep as he had leapt over the shieldwall.

Any normal cavalry attack would have swiftly dissolved into disorder, but these were Vanari soldiers. Such was the grace and balance of these white-armoured chevaliers that they carried on the charge, regrouping as they battered their way through one rank after another – even standing in the saddle so as to avoid the chopping blades that would otherwise dismember them. One, two, three aelven riders were pulled from their steeds, but the vast majority ploughed on, their momentum making them all but unstoppable. Lumineth spears found the torsos of Ossiarch soldiers time and again,

explosions of Hyshian light turning bony chests to ash. Those Mortek Guard at the rear of each echelon did not have time to set their spears or brace their shields, for with their Hekatos dead, they had no warning that the assault would be upon them with such shocking speed.

There was a whistling noise, descending fast. Suddenly, the Dawnrider Lance was thrown into disarray, bones exploding in all directions to shred stallions and hurl their riders broken into the dust. The Ossiarch catapults that had been stalking slowly forwards at the rear of the Mortek ranks had begun to rain fire into the thick of their own troops. It was a matter of pride to Horrek Venzai, the Liege-Kavalos who oversaw the garrison's reinforcement, that they meet the cavalry head to head. If they had to force their enemies into the open through the destruction of their comrades-in-arms, then so be it.

AVOWED RETRIBUTION

The wrath of the Ossiarchs was slow-burning, much like that of their master Nagash, but it had a deadly surety to it that even the Lumineth could not deny. This was their world, and any victory that the Realm-lords won here would be temporary. Still, the aelves fought on with hope in their hearts.

The next volley of catapult ammunition to hit home was not of iron-hard skulls but of strange runic cauldrons, each reverberating with the howls of the damned. They exploded in bursts of greenish energy and screaming banshees spilled from within, stopping the hearts of nearby Lumineth with the intensity of their rage and grief. Horse and rider alike keeled over, dead before they even hit the ground. As to the Mortek Guard, they were affected not at all by the killing screams; with the Lumineth reeling, they closed in and levelled their spears, jabbing and thrusting until large sections of the Dawnrider Lance lay bleeding in the dirt.

At a shout from the Regent Uthralle, the Dawnriders headed for open ground, but with enemy artillery hammering them, the habitual close order of the Dawnrider wedge was a crippling disadvantage.

In breaking formation, they lost momentum and gave the Mortek Guard the chance they needed to grind them to a halt. Shieldwalls clamped into place around the Dawnriders – this time twice as tall, one rank raising their shields high to rest upon those of another. Between the gaps, spears thrust four by four. The Ossiarchs closed in like the jaws of a blacksilt crocodile around the neck of a floundering gazellion, and in a matter of moments, their methodical onslaught had buckled the flanks of the Dawnrider assault. Fewer than half of the riders made it out alive; they galloped down the crumbling cliff edges of the bastion and onto the plains below, only to find the heavy cavalry of the Kavaloi bearing down upon them from the flatlands.

The shining companies of the Vanari, glorious in their white robes, and the Alarith Stoneguard,

stalwart enough to hold a position almost indefinitely, had made obvious targets. To man a fortress in Nagash's realm – even an improvised one – was an open challenge that could not go unanswered. Yet in engaging the Lumineth across such a wide frontage, the Ossiarchs had left their own strongholds defended at half strength. Here was the full power of the Realm-lords brought to bear. The Mage God had an agenda, and he had devised a dozen ways to make it happen.

A heat haze grew to the east of the Triptych. To the Ossiarchs scanning the horizon, it appeared as a mirage, then it shimmered into an ethereal illusion, and then, to the stupefaction of the Bonereapers, it became a three-pronged assault that looked very real indeed. In the distance was another metalith, one that had not so much crashed as settled in good order to allow a trident of Lumineth to drive in towards the Triptych. Closest was a spearhead of mountain spirits in their war forms; the ground shook to the ponderous thump of their footfalls as they closed the distance to the walls of the nearest fortress. Horrek Venzai's Deathriders wheeled around fast, thundering across the plains towards them, but they had been drawn out of position by the Dawnriders they had pursued scant minutes before. Already the Spirits of the Mountain were falling upon the furthermost tower, their enormous worldhammers brought to bear as a team of sappers might shatter the walls of a condemned building.

In moments, the walls of the fortress were crumbling, cascades of obsidian and iron-hard bone sloughing away to tumble across the wastes. Then came Vandaris, a true giant of an aelementor, for his mountain incarnation in Ymetrica scraped the skies. He swung his worldhammer, the head of which was the width of a scholar's spire, and smashed it with colossal force into the statue atop the fortress. With the walls collapsing, the entire structure shuddered and came crashing down into the dirt.

The next to fall was Fortress Zandtos. The winds howled ever louder around the towering edifice until they began to take form – they too had hidden their strength until the time was right. A hurtling figure blurred in the chill air, resolving more and more as it circled the vast statue of Zandtos. With each pass, it unleashed a glowing shaft of light that stabbed into the superstructure of the fortress in such a way as to weaken the whole. The defences had been built with painstaking care, but just as a skull or pelvis has fissures, they had architectural weak spots. As the gale of the figure's passage became a hurricane, then a cyclone, the fortress creaked, groaned and finally – in an avalanche of masonry – collapsed altogether.

Soaring high on a thermal of displaced magic, Teclis sent a triple ray of light searing from one outstretched hand. The beams carved through the rock of the statue as if it were made of wax, lopping off its arm and decapitating it soon after. Cut diagonally at the waist, the top half slid from the bottom with stately slowness before crashing hard into the phalanx of Ossiarchs marching beneath. With that, it was done.

The Mortisans that would have made repairs to their giant edifice were all burned to nothing, their remnants already mingling with the sandy earth. Without the deathly magic of their masters to invigorate them, the Ossiarch infantry had not the pace to close with Teclis' fellow Realm-lords. The aelves' statement had been made: though Katakros himself remained at large, his effigies had been torn down, and on a symbolic level, that was a victory in itself.

The archmage met Celennar's calm gaze for a moment, and fate seemed to click into place. He made the seventh sign, drawing his hands across the landscape and imagining the rune Yngra carved there as he intoned the words of power. And as he imagined it, it came to be. With each new rune emblazoned upon the land, another swathe of Shyish was cleansed of Nagash's twisted influence and forcibly returned to harmony. So it would be across all of the Amethyst Realm.

As the glowing rune dimmed, Teclis saw something glint in his mind's eye. He scanned the surviving Bonereapers below and noted that the aura surrounding one of them was stained black, in the manner of its master Nagash. The creature sensed his presence and spoke.

'God of light,' it said, the words blossoming in Teclis' mind. 'You know not that which you do. It is not too late to turn back.'

'I pity you,' said Teclis, his telepathy stabbing down with such force that the creature staggered within its strange coffin-like mantle. 'I did not depose Chaos only to see your master reshape reality in its stead.'

'Then so be it,' said the deathly figure. 'The gods will grind one another to dust, and the time of the immortals will be brought all the closer.'

Teclis gestured, making the rune of departure, and the Lumineth started to disengage, the ruin of the Triptych dust-covered in their wake.

'You think you are the first to topple these statues?' said the creature. 'Fool. You will find eternity a far better tutor than instinct.'

Vokmortian the Emissary scattered into black sand – and was gone.

23

A GRAND STRATEGY

With the battlelines drawn between the Lumineth and their new foes, a great game of conquest unfolded across the Ossiarch Empire, for Teclis intended his message of hope to spread far and wide. Here, the talent and vision of the Realm-lords was tested against the merciless strategy of Katakros' legions.

Equuis Main, the northernmost continent of the Ossiarch Empire, is noted for its endless, windswept plains and rugged steppes. It was ravaged by the forces of Khorne during the Age of Chaos, but the barbarian tribes of that time were eventually ground to nothing by Katakros' methodical advance, and the bones of those conquests were incorporated into the Stalliarch Lords who call that land home. Lumineth cavalry echelons had emerged from the Magthar portal, the Hurakan mages at their head speeding them across Praetoris by keeping the wind literally at their backs. Swiftly they advanced, bypassing the coastal fortresses of Xanda and Sinda altogether, and charging deep into the territory of the Stalliarchs.

That fleet warhost, gleaming in the darkness, did not go unnoticed by the spies of Liege-Kavalos Horrek Venzai. The Aviarch Spymasters sent out their messenger carrion birds from the Harshspurs, the birds wheeling high to gather information about the Lumineth invasion. Most of their number were shot from afar by keen-eyed Vanari archers or torn apart by cyclonic winds as the aelementiri of the Hurakan temples brought their influence to bear, but by then it was too late: the Spymasters can see through the eyes of their construct-birds, and already they knew that the Lumineth had established a significant presence across Equuis Main.

Seen from above, the cavalry columns of the Stalliarch Lords curved in towards the Lumineth riders like a claw closing around an outstretched limb. Each Kavalos Lance was a talon intended to gouge and tear before withdrawing to the main body of the Bonereapers army. Running battles erupted, feint and counter-feint unfolding at speed as the Lumineth matched their dexterity and swiftness against the undying resolve of their pursuers.

At first, the Dawnriders and their aelementiri comrades, the fast-riding Hurakan Windchargers, were able to outmanoeuvre the Ossiarchs. One column feigned flight whilst another, formerly running parallel, reined back to attack the rear of the Deathrider formations sent by Horrek Venzai to assail their comrades. They struck at speed, felling several of their foes with arrow and lance, only to swiftly withdraw before the spears of the Deathriders could exact revenge.

But even the steeds of Ymetrica tire eventually. After several days of riding hard, and after being forced into performing the most demanding manoeuvres by the unnatural skill of their adversaries, the Lumineth horsemasters gave the call for a true retreat. They galloped towards the Brass Mountains dividing Equuis Main north to south, the peaks of which had been transmuted to hot metal by the incursions of Khorne during the Age of Chaos. In doing so, they hoped to wrong-foot their pursuers, for the aelves reckoned that the mountainous terrain would be tough to traverse for the heavyset Ossiarch mounts, and that the higher they climbed, the more that would prove true. They believed that, once they reached the shoulders of the mountains, they would be able to recover and take stock of the war below.

They found no such respite. To the Stalliarch Lords, the thrill of the chase was the only pleasure left to them, and they pursued with maniacal intensity. Each Kavalos steed had been fashioned from bone taken not only from wild horses that feared nothing, but also from sure-footed mountain kuuatans and stony-skinned rhinoceroids. The brush and scree of the mountainside were of no more impediment to them than the arid wastes. Try as the flagging Lumineth might to outpace them, the Ossiarchs caught up; this time it was the nadirite spears of the Kavaloi that pierced the chests of their prey.

At the orders of Windspeaker Nerethai, the Hurakan riders, mounted on lithe treerunners as they were, evaded the Kavalos Deathriders and looped back down to the battle far beneath, leaving behind their Vanari comrades. They did so with heavy hearts, but with the Dawnriders' stallions wild-eyed and froth-skinned with exhaustion, they could run no more. Their riders formed a tight wedge in a gully, thinking to nullify their foes' advantage. It worked, for a time, allowing their last charge to drive so deep that they nearly struck down Kui-Nabzar, leader of the Equuis cavalry elite. But they failed at the last, outmatched by the Liege-Kavalos's sheer strength. As Hysh's glow dimmed in the skies, aelven bodies were cast into the dust of the mountain passes. Wordlessly, Kui-Nabzar and his Ossiarch riders stripped them, slung them across the backs of their gore-stained steeds and rode back to their necropolis strongholds. The armour and gemstones of the Lumineth they left to languish – they had little use for them, though they had a hundred uses for the dead.

THE LIVING HURRICANE

A small strike force of Hurakan riders had been sent to Cadavaris, that land to the south of Praetoris. Their intent was not to engage the Ossiarchs in open battle but to destabilise and confound. The Hurakan Windmage who led their mission, known as Lord Djarian the Sighing Light, led his warriors past the towering citadel of Nerozzar at speed – such speed, in fact, that the Mortek Crawlers atop the battlements could not hit them even when leading their shots as per the commands of their war viziers. Khebukhan, the Ossiarch liege who garrisoned the mighty citadel's upper spires, could not abide the concept that enemy riders could wander at will outside his walls. He sent a message, via his Mortisan priests, to the Sinistral Master of the Petrifex Elite. An old ally of his since the Purge of Marachia, the Sinistral Master was to intercept the wind-riding aelves as they headed over the Spinatar Bridge, which crossed the Pentaghul River to the west of Nerozzar and was the swiftest way from the north of the region to the south. The Sinistral Master conjured a great mist, yellowish-grey and foul, made from the by-products of those souls he had stripped in the course of his grisly arts. He set it about the banks of the Pentaghul and had his towering Petrifex constructs stamp into place on the far side. According to Khebukhan, the Lumineth would ride hard through their position in a matter of moments.

Sure enough, they were bound for that site, but the brethren of the Hurakan temples have little need for such quotidian measures as bridges. As they neared the river's edge, Lord Djarian summoned a howling gale to attend him. This gale was no natural wind: it was the capricious spirit known as Xenthe the Revealer, and it drove back the greyish-yellow mist that the Sinistral Master had summoned. As the black and stony skeletons of the Petrifex loomed out from the mist, the Windchargers took their shots, arrows arcing across the river, aiming not at their foes' necks, nor at their empty eye sockets, but at their chests.

A normal arrow would have rebounded from the iron-hard bone that covered each sternum; even that of a Vanari Auralan Sentinel would not have burned its way through to strike the soul-trap gems within. Yet the arrows of the Hurakan were borne upon sentient winds. They veered to fly directly upwards as they neared the towering constructs, then, as the gale-force winds that bore them reversed direction, they shot vertically down. Their tips, placed with pinpoint accuracy by the winds, penetrated the tiny weak spots behind the giant constructs' collarbones to strike their soultrap gems, destroying them completely. One of the constructs fell, then two, then ten. The Hurakan Windchargers rode hard for the gap, the edge of the stinking, greenish river getting ever closer. Then Lord Djarian gave a great shout, and he and his brethren were lifted from the ground, the wind Xenthe turning their leap of faith into a high glide, before they alighted on the other side of the river where the Petrifex Elite had fallen. As they passed, they gathered up the heads of the constructs they had slain, and with a whispered word in the ear of their riding beasts, sprinted through the mist to evade the stamping, rock-hard monstrosities closing in upon them.

In a trice, they were gone. But the echoes of their deeds were not. Making haste to the city of Xalacar, three of their number took the news of the Petrifex defeat to the armies of the living locked in a struggle for southern Cadaveris. Three more raced back up the Necrarch Coast, taking the heads of the fallen constructs to the human city of Glymmsforge in Lyria. A third team took their own outsized trophies to the city of Lethis, leaping nimbly over the anti-gheist wards of the city to bear the message of hope to the humans rebuilding within. The Ossiarchs could be beaten – even the largest and toughest of their number – and the allies of Sigmar's pantheon were here to help. It was a message that lit the fires of hope in a hundred thousand human hearts, and it spread further with each new day.

IN VICTORY, DEFEAT

The Lumineth had won several major victories across the Ossiarch Empire, all symbolic in nature. The Realm-lords had never intended to take territory from their foes; they purely wished to show that the scions of Nagash were not invulnerable and that their grave-cold grip on the realms could be broken.

The Hyshians know well the value of hope and the flame of defiance that burns in the hearts of mortals – if that spark goes out, despair can follow. With the Age of Chaos making its curse felt across the realm and the forces of Death resurgent, the people of Shyish had found their inner fires guttering. In many places, this death of hope had seen the very underworlds in which they lived crumble and fall away into the depths of the Shyish Nadir. They were caught between the immovable object of Nagash's empire and the unstoppable force of the Chaos invaders that sought to retake those lands they had once claimed; in such times, even a meagre optimism was all but impossible. It was this that the Lumineth sought to address – not by attacking the Ossiarchs' domains, not by taking the holdings of Nagash for themselves, but by putting the lie to the very notion of the inevitable victory of Death.

The Lumineth had brought another gift to the people of Shyish – the geomantic magic with which they had scorched their mark onto the underworlds themselves. On the open plains, the rolling foothills, even emblazoned on the bottom of shallow lakes, the sigils of the aelven race burned bright. Much in evidence was the symbol Yngra, the rune of rescue but also of imprisonment. It was a double meaning that had especial resonance here, for whilst the runes protected the inhabitants of the underworlds against an all-consuming darkness of the soul, they also pinned those benighted domains in place, making it all but impossible for them to shift on a cosmological scale. This dual defence against the constant pull of the Shyish Nadir meant that those underworlds were effectively saved from the parasitic hunger of Nagash's masterwork.

However, the Lumineth had failed to account for the nature of the Ossiarch Bonereapers. They did not fully appreciate the fact that the harder Nagash's chosen were struck, the more determined their masters would be to strike back. This was no foe they could defeat swiftly and efficiently; it was a dread nemesis that they would never be rid of. On a purely material level, the more the Lumineth gave their lives to break Ossiarch rule, the more power they granted them. Already the corpses of the aelves that had been deemed irretrievable were being gathered up in a dozen theatres of war, taken back to the Mortisan

priesthood in the great fortresses of bone that formed their strongholds and remade into new warriors. The Boneshapers received these bodies gladly, for aelf bone is of fine quality indeed – flexible and light, it retains its strength for centuries without blemish. The lithe war-creatures they fashioned from the remains of their enemies would be possessed of a fearsome alacrity.

It was not only the bodily remains of the aelves that were harnessed by the Mortisans, of course, but also the very souls of those whom they had slain. Taken from the corpses of the dying before they could depart, the aelf-souls were sequestered into flasks and blended with those of choice human prey, forming animating essences that were quick of thought yet bellicose and aggressive in a way the contemplative aelves of Hysh could never be. It was an exquisite form of torture for the aelf-souls so treated; revering purity above all, they considered the blending of human essence with their superior aelven animus to be a ghastly dilution that would trap them in purgatory – even before being interred in a body of stolen bone. It was a fate that Nagash took great pleasure in gloating over, for he knew the aelf psyche well, and he had every intention of inflicting his twisted form of punishment upon every Lumineth that had dared stray into his domain. If these intruders loved the human denizens so much, then let them become one and the same. They would serve in the very armies they sought to defy for the rest of eternity. It was as malicious a fate as Nagash could deliver at that point, and his Mortisans were more than happy to make it a reality, but already the Supreme Lord of Undeath was laying plans for a more lasting and grandiose revenge…

The void between worlds was a lonely place, somewhere in between a silvery shimmer and a deep, silent pitch black. It was one of the reasons Teclis enjoyed it so much.

Here, he could let his gaze bore through time and space, finding answers within the complex weave between the two. This day, with his mind's eye, he looked upon Ghyran. He had to squint, so as not to be sickened in body and soul by the vileness that had all but claimed it. But if he concentrated for long enough, he could see a glimmer of true green, taste the sticky tang of fresh sap and hear the unsullied song of nature.

In that song, Alarielle came to him.

'Brother,' she said, her voice the urgent whisper of a spring wind. 'You transgress.'

'I have no choice,' said Teclis, acknowledging the double meaning with a slight elevation of his chin. 'Was I to let those Shyishan underworlds fall one by one? Was I to let the Necromancer remake reality without intervention?'

'You start a new front when the greater war hangs in the balance.'

'Time,' said Teclis, 'is the greatest enemy of all.'

'Not necessarily,' said Alarielle. 'Spring is coming, as it always does. No need to force it.'

'I am ensuring it comes whilst it still can,' said Teclis. 'And what are you doing, sister?'

'Preparing the way,' she said, her eyes narrowing. 'The realms themselves are awakening, and they are most puissant of all. My agents work to guide their wrath.'

'Even as I pacify, you seek to inflame.'

'I seek to free, Teclis. To give back. You do not see all, brother, despite your pretensions. Even now there is a traitor within your ranks.'

Teclis kept his features a mask of serenity.

'I thank you for the warning. Yet I shall not deviate. The Necromancer's grip is strong, but it is slow to close. The curse of death will be lifted.'

'And the resurgence of life will begin.'

'Life, and light,' said Teclis. 'As ever united.'

'Of course,' said Alarielle.

'You too risk unleashing energies that even you cannot control,' said Teclis.

'A bold judgement, given the speed of your current course. You realise you goad the dragon?'

'I do. Yet where Hysh can take the punishment, Shyish cannot.'

Alarielle shook her head in disgust. 'Then follow your blind man's path, and see the darkness to which it leads. I will not aid you.'

'I would not ask for your aid,' said Teclis. 'I know you too well.'

Alarielle turned, her face cast in sorrow, and was gone.

ACT II
WAR
OF THE
MORTARCHS

INVASION OF INVIDIA

Nagash entrusted the duty of spreading the power of the Shyish Nadir to his Mortarchs, for only they amongst his servants had the magical ability to attempt such a metaphysical feat. Mannfred von Carstein was to bring the curse of endings to Ghyran's Everspring Swathe – though his schemes would be far from unopposed.

Every realm has its arcane portals into the Realm of Death. Most of the departed find their souls awakening there, of course, but there are ways for the living – and the unliving, come to that – to pass to and from Shyish. Nagash commanded his Mortarchs to find those gates near populous areas of the realms and use the artifice of necromantic magic to bring about their demise. In this way, he would not only collapse the realmgate but create a lesser Nadir in its place, an arcane sinkhole connected to the all-consuming Shyish Nadir that is the end of all things. Slowly, inevitably, the energy and vitality of the realm about each collapsed portal would be sucked dry, its people claimed by the Nadir. The realm of Hysh was to feel the dread touch of Nagash most of all, for the Lumineth had earned his ire. First to be invaded, however, was the Everspring Swathe in Ghyran, a land of corrupted natural splendour.

BLEEDING GATE
This portal to Shyish, once framed by carven sapvines, has become a rotten mockery of life.

Those realms that Nagash had identified as targets for his grand experiment were very different in nature. Ghyran was perhaps the most difficult of all to conquer, for it was so thoroughly infested with the power of the Plaguefather, Nurgle, that its once verdant fields had degenerated into sucking quagmires, stinking bogs and suppurating sores of colossal size. The land itself was sick, and any who strayed within risked contracting the direst plagues.

Arkhan had been entrusted with bringing the power of the Shyish Nadir to the Realm of Light – a land of haunted deserts, magical symbolism and toppled spires. When Mannfred von Carstein's Legion of Night was given the duty of invading Ghyran, his fellow Mortarchs did not hide their amusement. Neferata openly smirked, for she had been tasked

with taking Nagash's conquests into Chamon – though beset by the change-kin forces of Tzeentch, it was at least a realm of glittering potential, and her spies had long infiltrated its heart. Better yet, she had agents in the vampire-hunting Order of Azyr – amongst them the notorious Jelsen Darrock – who would wreak havoc in Mannfred's kingdom of Carstinia whilst her rival and neighbour was absent.

Mannfred did not protest at the duty Nagash had given him; he merely bowed, every inch the humble servant. In this seeming misfortune, as in so many other things, the vampire lord saw hidden opportunity. A plan unfolded in his mind, one that perhaps only a von Carstein could have conceived – and one that likely only Mannfred, most treacherous of all his kin, could have made a reality.

GASTROBOMINUS SLUDGE
The once bucolic cliffs overlooking the Sickling Sea are drenched in daemonic slime.

TOXIC IRRIGATIONS
The Reality Sores are surrounded by rivers of bubbling, gore-laced effluent.

DEATH INTO LIFE

Mannfred von Carstein has seen his fortunes rise and fall a dozen times over the long centuries of his existence. Yet he has survived, earning a place at the high table in Nagash's court. More than that, he commands an entire legion of the dead. It was that army that marched forth into Ghyran.

The largest portal to Shyish in the Everspring Swathe was the Bleeding Gate. This was a moss-draped ring of arcane architecture that had once, in the Age of Myth, been glorious to look upon. When Horticulous Slimux had conquered the surrounding area, it had been reduced to a slimy, dripping mess. The rock itself wept dark gore in protest against the corrupting influence of Nurgle that had enveloped it, and the vegetation around it was withered and black. It was a place where the energies of death waxed strong; to one with the witch-sight, motes of amethyst magic billowed through from Shyish every so often, wheezing out like the sighs of a dying drake.

It was from this portal that Mannfred von Carstein emerged into the sucking quagmires of Invidia. He found the land distasteful, but not so much so that he could not bear to be there. In places, it was much like the land of his birth, a demesne whose macabre castles were surrounded by rotting, squelching moorland and mud-filled ditches. Borne upon the broad back of his dread abyssal, Ashigaroth, Mannfred was kept from the ignominy of having to wade through the ruin-dotted swamps – though the thumb-sized mosquitoes that sought his blood were a constant inconvenience. At first, he chuckled whenever their probosces breached his pallid skin, for they burst under the sheer potency of his vitae, but when his skin became slick with gore, his sardonic humour evaporated. Summoning the chill of the grave to keep the insects at bay, he sought the scent of human blood upon the wind. It was not long before he found it. To the north, situated along the Minuet Rivers, were primitive swamp tribes that had thrown their lot in with Nurgle. They considered the Bleeding Gate to be a place of ill omen, and they were soon to be proved right. Mannfred led an echelon of armoured wights against them, a force that cared no more about the dangers and diseases of the swamps than a scarecrow cares about the wind.

For every skeletal warrior that traipsed though the waist-deep water in a rough semblance of good military order, there were two more beneath the surface to the flanks, crawling along the murky bed through the swampwater or hauling themselves through the weeds with untiring stamina. The dead care not for comfort, nor even for drawing breath – a fact that Mannfred had used to his advantage countless times, most notably against the Flyblown Legion in Rotsoul Mire, a place not unlike Invidia itself.

The patrol of wights, intended to lure any potential threats out from hiding, came under attack on several occasions as it made its way north. Massive, blotch-skinned Plague Toads belched and bubbled as they lashed the passing skeletons with thick muscular tongues; each was spitted and hoisted high by Mannfred's fleshless warriors before it could do too much damage. Gibbering Jabberslythes reared up from the swamp, their sheer hideousness enough to drive a man to the edge of sanity, yet their maddening aura had no effect on the armoured wights that endured their teeth and claws. These creatures Mannfred dispatched personally, the vorpal edge of Gheistvor taking their heads as he swooped down from above. The swamp tribes, though they ambushed the intruders with jagged spear and poisoned javelin, were soon subjugated, for Mannfred attacked in the dead of night and visibility was almost nil. Many swamp-braves were unmanned by sheer terror; bound by skeletal hands, they were brought back to the Bleeding Gate. There they were sacrificed to Nagash, their screams and thrashing escape attempts as nothing to the wights that held them down for the executioner's blades.

With their departing essences bound to his cause, Mannfred began the work Nagash had entrusted to him: weaving a potent necromantic enchantment upon the Bleeding Gate itself. It was a spell similar in nature to the Curse of Years, which, in the space of a few agonising seconds, could age a warrior to dotage, then to a withered skeleton, and then to a scattering of dust. When complete, the spell would crumble masonry and turn mortar that had stood the test of aeons to powder until there was nothing left of the runic structure that held the portal sacrosanct. With the energies of Shyish in such concentration, a master of magic such as Mannfred could bring about the realmgate's end with shocking speed and open a yawning black void in its stead – a hundredth as potent as the Shyish Nadir, this sinkhole would be linked to its metaphysical twin and would channel its dread hunger. Taking a moment, Mannfred frowned. The bait was in place. But without heavy resistance, his true plan would be over before it began.

A GARDENER'S REVENGE

To the south-east of the Bleeding Gate was a region known as the Claim of Horticulous. It was a giant tract of land, dozens of leagues across, that surrounded the three massive lakes of putrescence known as the Reality Sores. It abutted the Toxic Irrigations in the south and the Gastrobominus Sludge in the east, that coastal region thoroughly corrupted by the minions of Nurgle's first Herald, Horticulous Slimux. A nation belonging to the Plague God more than it did Ghyran, the annex was the pride of the daemon Herald, a portion of his master's garden made real in the lands of men. Horticulous had not managed to claim all of Invidia – he had resigned himself to leaving the Bleeding Gate well alone, for nothing would grow near it, and its aura of deathly energy affected even him. The rest of the landmass, however, was under his care. So it was that when the balance of life and death began to change in the domains under his purview, he was quick to notice. With the portal's innate Shyishan energies concentrated by Mannfred's spell, the pall of death was spreading ever further. Horticulous's prized gardens were beginning to blacken and wither, and that was a transgression he could not stand – he and his rival Rotigus had their fill of Shyishan magic during the Time of Tribulations not so long ago.

Mannfred von Carstein was no fool. He knew full well that the daemons of Nurgle would trudge forth in great numbers to hurl back his invasion. More than that, he knew they were slow, and like all the forces of the Chaos Gods, they had their own obsessions and blind spots. Entrusting leadership to three Soulblight vampires he had sired in distant Carstinia, he sent forth a triple-pronged assault to make a pre-emptive strike against the forces of Nurgle. They were to attack the Reality Sores at the same time but from different angles, a concerted attack upon the

heartlands of Horticulous's domain. Mannfred knew from his travails against the Flyblown Legion that the number three was pleasing to Nurgle; the icon of the Plaguefather had three lobes, just as the Reality Sores comprised three discrete lakes from which the plague-hosts emerged. Yet though Mannfred sent three large, obvious armies to attack, his fourth and most potent force was the one entrusted with the greatest duty of all – that of the guardian rather than the invader.

The first of Mannfred's armies was a hundreds-strong host of Deadwalkers led by the floating bone-construct known as the Beacon Mortis. This army was self-replenishing; glowing with the power of necromancy, the relic at its heart drew forth the long-drowned from beneath the water's surface to join the horde. Slimux sent not Plaguebearers to intercept the shambling mass but his flolloping, splashing Beasts of Nurgle, despatching them as a farmer sends dogs to hound sheep. The heavyset beasts did not engage the trespassers in combat so much as flatten them, ignoring the slashing of rusted blades to bodily slam the undead apart in their enthusiasm to join in the fun. Over the course of a long day of battle, the Deadwalker host was decimated, despite being resurrected time and time again by the Beacon Mortis. Still, the host had fulfilled its purpose as a distraction.

The second army was intercepted not by Slimux but by his old ally and rival, Rotigus. The obese immensity had been wandering the Sliming Woad at the time of Mannfred's incursion, and he had headed north towards the Bleeding Gate as soon as he had sensed a powerful magical presence there. Sloshing through the quagmires amidst a throng of Plaguebearers and burbling, flatulent Nurglings, the daemon's slow, deliberate progress was halted by a

MANNFRED VON CARSTEIN

Mannfred is the last remnant of an infamous Soulblight dynasty hailing from the World-that-Was. As a vampire lord, he lingered in the shadow of the von Carstein family's eldest, whose autocratic rule saw him deny Mannfred time and again. At the end of the cataclysm that was the End Times, Mannfred cut down the one man that could perhaps have averted the catastrophe. It was a spiteful gesture, intended only to harm, yet it appealed to Nagash's sense of bitter justice. Here was a soul who would commit any act, no matter how destructive, in the furtherance of his own goals – a kindred spirit, of sorts. When the Great Necromancer gained power over Shyish, he took what was left of Mannfred's tortured soul and remade his body from the clay of undeath. He took pains to ensure the von Carstein did not transcend the curse in his blood, however, for he wanted no peace for those who would wage his wars. Since then, Mannfred has channelled his simmering rage into dozens of conquests in Nagash's name.

barrow-host waiting for him near the undulating hills of the Claim of Horticulous. A thousand witchlights lit the eye sockets of the skeletal horde. They had the stench of death about them, but what would have been a sumptuous bouquet of rot had been reduced to horrible sterility by the necromancy that animated them. As the skeleton army fought wordlessly to encircle Rotigus's carnivalesque procession, the Great Unclean One bellied low in the water and summoned forth a flood – not from the swollen skies but from the swamp about him. Bringing his flabby arms around in great sweeping arcs, he triggered a tsunami of filth that crashed into the skeletons and bowled them backwards. He thought them dealt with, for a while, but they rose dripping from the depths to attack his daemons over and over again until the two armies were forced into a grinding war of attrition.

The third undead army to advance upon the Reality Sores came from the Hind Sea. Riding deep into the hagfish-choked waters, the host of mounted wights that formed the army's spearhead rode their skeletal steeds along the silty seabed along the length of the Gastrobominus Sludge. When they reached their designated muster point – the promontory to the east of the Grimscale Peaks – they rode up the pebbled beach and into the lands to the north. In doing so, they gave the impression that Mannfred's army had inveigled itself into multiple regions of Invidia.

Horticulous Slimux, having anticipated a sly attack on his central holdings even as his vanguard was engaged to the north, gathered his fellow Heralds and moved to block the cavalry force encroaching on his domain. With him went the Spoilpox Scrivener known as Noddrack the Snitch and the capering Sloppity Bilepiper called Gortle Pulpskull, whose rude limericks were much beloved of Slimux's Nurglings – if not the ancient gardener himself. Together, the three Heralds mustered a tripartite defence, a bulwark of daemon flesh that stretched back half a mile from the front line and could draw on near limitless reinforcements from the Reality Sores. The Black Knights sent to harry them crashed home against a nigh-immovable wall of Plaguebearers, their lances bursting through chests and swollen guts before they were dragged from their skeleton steeds. In a matter of hours, they were defeated utterly. But in buying Mannfred time, they had achieved their purpose.

FROM THE GREEN THEY CAME

Mannfred's ritual proceeded undisturbed, the brutal sacrifice of the Nurgle-worshipping swamp tribes charging the air to saturate the Bleeding Gate with the energies of death. The realmgate began to

crumble; in doing so, it spread the billowing magic of necromancy across the heartlands of the Everspring Swathe. But it was not just the forces of Nurgle that sought to stymie this new peril. To the west, a far more aggressive and vital force was making its way to the Bleeding Gate.

The Sylvaneth of Ghyran are hyper-sensitive to the flow of life and death in their native realm, and none more so than Alarielle the Everqueen. She had become emotionally inured to the sickening effects of Nurgle upon her realm; where once they spurred despair, now they elicited only rage. Yet there was now a new note in the spirit-song of the land. It was a mournful dirge, its elegiac tones synonymous not with the cyclical, nightmarish parody of the natural order that was Nurgle but with the forces of Death itself. The land of Invidia had long been corrupted by the daemon Slimux, but now something sought to drain it of all life, fair or foul. If allowed to continue unabated, this force would spread its sucking malignancy across the Everspring Swathe and beyond. That was something Alarielle could not allow. She sensed the cold hand of the Great Necromancer behind the plan; this was a feat within his reach, though he acted through one of his Mortarch puppets. More than that, he acted through none other than Mannfred von Carstein, a devious vampire whom she hated more than any other servant of Nagash.

During the twilight years of the World-that-Was, Mannfred had captured the aelf princess Aliathra. The daughter of Alarielle and Tyrion – who, though now estranged as gods, were paramours in mortal life – Aliathra was a potent figure. As a captive, her blood was used to empower a dark ritual during Mannfred's quest to raise Nagash from his long torpor. Millennia later, Alarielle's divinations had revealed that the very same vampire was planning another ritual in the lands she had once called her own – and one empowered by a mass sacrifice at that.

The spirit paths of the Sylvaneth pass through the magical veins of the lands themselves, and this is especially true of Ghyran. Attuning herself and her spirit-revenant followers to the lament of the lands, the Everqueen stepped into a magical vale in Verdia – and emerged in the still-verdant reaches of Prince's Contention, those lands north of the Minuet Rivers that had as yet remained unsullied by Slimux and his allies. She made haste south, parting the waters of those rivers that barred her path with a wave of her hand. Anything that stood in her way was pitilessly destroyed by her Treelord escort; this day, Alarielle brought nature's wrath to bear and gave nothing in return.

With his three-pronged attack locked in battle far to the south, slowly being driven backwards by the assaults of Rotigus, Horticulous Slimux and a numberless horde of plague daemons, Mannfred faced the prospect of a war on two fronts as the vengeful forces of the Sylvaneth waded through the muck of the Minuet riverbed and climbed the banks to assail the Beasts of Nurgle gambolling beyond.

Before the hour was out, each host was covered in blackish-green mud, Kurnoth Hunters wrestling with wriggling, slug-like daemon beasts that spurted slime every time an oak-hard talon pierced their hides. The exception was Alarielle herself, whose leafy wings carried her aloft as her wardroth beetle, transformed into a host of glowing fireflies, glittered around her. Wherever her gaze fell, natural life blossomed and the touch of Nurgle was undone. Those men of the swamp tribes who had not been captured by Mannfred attacked the Sylvaneth flanks with impressive fervour, for the daemons that stalked the land were as sure a sign of Nurgle's favour as they could ever hope for. No pity did Alarielle hold in her heart for such Chaos-tainted fools. She gestured with the half-oaken talon that formed her left arm, and one by one the swamp tribesmen hardened into wood, twisting and putting down roots until a grove of saplings stood where a band of warriors had existed moments before.

Through corrupted thicket and black-hearted forest Alarielle forged her path of redemption, the evil magic of Nurgle sloughing away with the sheer force of her wrath. Where the daemons gathered thick to stop her, she would scatter magical pollens; these took form as shrieking Dryads that stabbed and tore the toughened hide of Nurgle's footsoldiers as if it were dried parchment. Nevertheless, she saved the greater part of her rage for the forces of undeath.

Seeing the Everqueen's light growing closer with every passing hour, Mannfred sent the vampire lord Garathrac the Skull-Hound against her. He did not expect the Soulblight warlord to defeat the Everqueen, despite the fact that Garathrac had lately posited the concept that his mastery over his prized trio of Zombie Dragons made him the equal of a god of war – a notion soon to be proven false. As Alarielle took out her rage upon Garathrac and his undead drakes, Mannfred engaged her from a distance, casting a spell of dark magic upon her. It turned the Everqueen's wings black and withered her skin, but even as Mannfred watched, the goddess of life regrew to her former splendour. Meanwhile, the first of Garathrac's

winged beasts was spitted on the antlers of Alarielle's wardroth beetle; the second was impaled by the Spear of Kurnoth, which turned the drake into a scattering of moths that fluttered away into the night; and the last, which bore Garathrac himself, was caught up in a copse of trees that came suddenly alive to rip both beast and rider apart in a flurry of violence. Worse yet, the hosts of Horticulous had appeared on the other horizon. Mannfred's necromantic ritual had been broken by Alarielle's magic, as he had suspected it would be. Sketching a bow towards the goddess, the Mortarch retreated through the Bleeding Gate, leaving his forces to cover his escape.

ALL THAT GLITTERS

The Mortarch entrusted with bringing the Shyish Nadir's hunger to Chamon was Neferata, the queen of the Nulahmian courts. Her instincts for subterfuge served her well – were it not for the dogged investigatory work of a lone Kharadron shipmistress, she might have concluded her work before any force could stop her.

Neferata's invasion of the Spiral Crux was meticulously planned and executed with the deadly competence that was her hallmark. Those lands were the stronghold of the Kharadron Overlords, and with good reason – ever since the cataclysm that had befallen the Spiral Crux, there was a great wealth of magic to be harnessed there. It was no secret that the Kharadron were motivated by profit above all else, and with a kingdom of riches with which to bribe them, Neferata had agents enough to influence the events there. At the time of her invasion of the Great Bewilderness, a stealth insertion waged in the dead of night, the eyes of the Kharadron were averted. She had chosen a remote locale from which to make her play, and those few sky-fleets that might have patrolled that area had, for some time, been persuaded to look for their bounty elsewhere. At the head of a great undead assemblage, the

Nulahmian queen emerged from the pitch-black disc of the Switchsoul Dais, a realmgate known only to the dead that shimmered deep beneath the Granthium Mountains. Flanked on either side by the coteries of vampires that were the bloodseeker connoisseurs and royal handmaidens of Neferatia, she advanced in splendour, but not a single word was spoken nor clarion herald's call heard. Here, Neferata would win her victory through secrecy and cunning – not brute force.

Were it not for the perspicacity of a young Kharadron admiral, the Mortarch Neferata would have secured the Switchsoul Dais's obsidian portal and had her ritual of corruption halfway to completion before any force above ground could have stopped her. Unlike Mannfred, she had ascertained exactly what it would take to collapse the realmgate portal and had brought

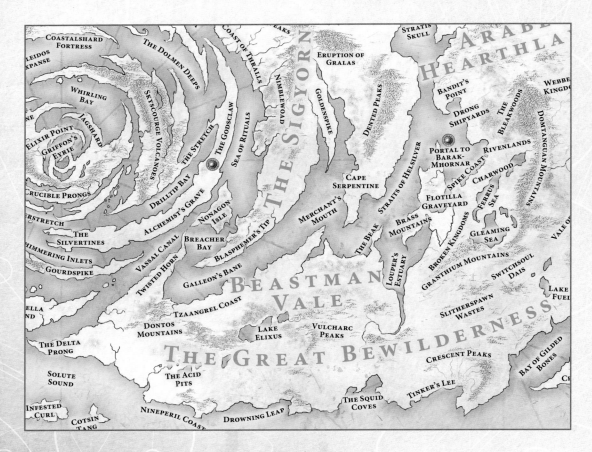

QUEEN NEFERATA

A consummate spymaster and queen of undeath, Neferata was the first to bear the Soulblight curse. It was her creation of an elixir distilled from the dark magic of Nagash that saw the Nehekharan become a new breed of undead, one whose immortality was bought at a terrible price – the need to drink blood for sustenance. Ever since Nagash revived her in the Mortal Realms, she has spread that curse across nations, founded dynasties, infiltrated the Cities of Sigmar and shaped a Shyishan nation in her own vision of grandeur. She is a regal and impressive figure; to lay eyes upon her is to feel a shiver of unworthiness, and to lock her gaze is to risk being forever lost. Queen Neferata has a network of handmaidens, agents and insiders that stretches across the Mortal Realms; their correspondence – be it magical or otherwise – is the lifeblood of her empire. Yet those who attack her, thinking her a creature of shallow luxury, are fatally mistaken, for she is quicksilver-fast as a striking asp.

the precise number of human sacrifices needed with her – plus thirty percent in case of mishap. Oiled, manacled and tattooed with Neferatian runes of obedience, these browbeaten slaves were driven forth from her stronghold in Nulahmia at the point of a spear by her skeletal elite. Forced to kneel in the darkness, the humans whimpered in fear, sensing what was to come. Yet not all of them would meet their end in that dank cavern.

Imoda Barrasdottr was an up-and-coming admiral in Kharadron society. She was respected more for her mastery of cartography than for her fleet, which only boasted a single Ironclad – the *Intaglio* – and a pair of Frigates. The walls of her war cabin, however, were military assets in themselves. Here Imoda had extensive maps of the Spiral Crux and the aerial aether-gold seams that swirled across it – outdated by the tumultuous effects of the necroquake but extensively amended ever since. Imoda knew them better than she did the faces of her crew. She had bartered, coerced, pried and eavesdropped for information in many sky-ports, talking not only to duardin of all stripes but also to humans and even a pair of itinerant aelves – travelling twins from Hysh with a strange charisma about them – until she had the headings and mine-routes of her contemporaries and their allies all mapped out, red cord criss-crossing across her beloved charts.

One night, deep in her prospector's studies and three flagons of magmalt ale in, she noticed that there was an area of the Granthium Mountains that none of her fellows passed through. At first, it had appeared simply to be an omission, but the more she looked at it, the more obvious it became that the area was being intentionally avoided. Several miner fleets had changed course before entering the region, despite

the fact that the swiftest route to their destination would have been straight through it. She frowned deeply and muttered her strongest oath. Someone or something wanted that area left alone, and they had the influence to make sure of it.

That very night, Admiral Barrasdottr ordered her meagre fleet on a new heading. Operating out of Barak-Zilfin, she crossed the Ferrus and Gleaming Seas, expertly avoiding the harkraken eyries en route and reaching the Granthium Mountains in good speed. Peering through her aethermatic spyglass, she saw something unusual between the spurs of a jagged double peak in the high passes – a human skeleton, not slumped in some hunter's lair but standing upright with its hollow eye sockets boring into hers. The revenant seemed to detect her scrutiny and turned slowly to move away. Ordering First Mate Grutti Fadrunsdotr to hand over her aethershot rifle, she lined up a shot and blasted a hole through the ribcage of the skeleton, sending it tumbling into a snowbank. As she handed the rifle back, she caught a glimpse of movement and watched, incredulous, as the skeleton got to its feet. Ribs dangling, it walked away at an unhurried pace, vanishing from sight into a fissure in the rock before Grutti could put it down.

Barrasdottr ordered the *Intaglio* and its escorts to come in low and, accompanied by a small detail of Arkanauts bolstered by Grundstok Thunderers, she followed the reanimated skeleton into the shadows beyond. Dark, confined spaces held no fear for the Kharadron that made their way down there. Stopping every so often to take measurements with her thaumic devices, Barrasdottr heard an echo of screams in the depths, abruptly cut short. Making solemn eye contact with her shipmates, she ventured further in.

What Imoda Barrasdottr found down there shocked her to her core. She got out again with her life – but only just – and her hair was turned white from root to tip. She carried Grutti the last few hundred yards, for the first mate's leg had been horribly mauled. They regained the *Intaglio* at the mountaintop and cast off, making haste for Barak-Zilfin. En route, they were attacked time and time again by massive, dark-winged creatures that had followed them from the cave; both Frigate escorts were pulled from the skies and their crew cast to their deaths when their endrins were clawed into uselessness. Were it not for the *Intaglio* braving the harkraken lairs – in doing so, rousing the beasts and setting them against the hell-bats and undead dragons that pursued them – they might never have made it. But as it was, Barrasdottr managed to reach the safety of Barak-Zilfin's alehouses, effectively bankrupt but still alive.

It was there that she told her story to the pair of aelves whom she had met before her grim discovery. They listened with intense interest, their wry smiles falling from their faces when Barrasdottr described a pallid queen of the dead atop a monstrous bone steed, working some manner of sacrifice in the depths. Had the creature not been entirely absorbed in the spell it was working, Barrasdottr felt she would have died then and there. As it was, she felt she had been aged ten years by the experience – at this, the aelves shared a meaningful glance.

Those aelves were Ellania and Ellathor, twin warsages that had roamed far from Hysh. The siblings had studied at the aetherquartz-rich Tower of Prios, and knew well of Hyshian magic's efficacy against Nagash's vile works. Though their home was the road, they had great influence in the courts of the Lumineth and knew a way to commune with them even across the cosmos. Ellania waited until dusk before climbing to the highest reaches of Barak-Zilfin; having earned the favour of the sky-port's admiralty by imparting priceless knowledge as to the whereabouts of the Baaeri Seam, she did so with little fear of being sent toppling back down by a volley of aethershot. From there, she could see the moon Celennar in the sky, dimly glinting as it reflected the brilliance of Hysh. Over the course of that night, she conferred with the moon-essence on a spiritual level. Her divinations had been borne out and their long journey to Chamon vindicated. Nagash planned to drain the life from the Spiral Crux under the very noses of the forces of civilisation.

With Celennar in close communion with Teclis, the Lumineth of Ymetrica were swift to respond. A reserve force of Alarith warriors, stepping from the stone gateways in Avalenoria into a portal leading to the Domtanguan Mountains, made haste to rendezvous with the twins in the Vale of Golden Idols to the east of the Gleaming Sea. Their meeting with Ellania and Ellathor was one of quiet celebration, for the leader of the strike force, the Stonemage Xelathuria, knew the siblings of old and had spoken of their potential to her elders.

The Alarith were a force of subtlety as well as strength. The lands thereabouts were infested with Tzaangors, yet through the use of hidden pathways, they had met the young siblings without incident. Into the Granthium Mountains they went, climbing hard to reach the double peak of which Admiral Barrasdottr had spoken. They prayed that they would still be in time to stop the deathly ritual, but given that the plant life of the mountain was withered and black for miles around, they feared they were already too late.

The thin passageways of the Granthium heights were stained with blood – and relatively fresh at that. Here and there, they encountered the ravaged corpses of the Kharadron excursion party that had gone before them, already half eaten by the verminous bats that flitted about, screaming shrilly at the Lumineth's intrusion. This time, the light was provided not by aethermatic endrins but by the Realm-lords themselves. Ellania and Ellathor glowed faintly in the darkness, the heightened senses of the aelves making it easy enough to see where they were going and keep their footing even when the tunnels became jagged and uneven. Further into the mountains they went until the faint sound of chanting lingered on the cusp of hearing. It was a dialect that Ellathor recognised from his studies of Teclian lore – an ancient tongue from another world known as Nehekharan.

The sense of oppression and morbidity that filled those caverns was palpable. Here was a potent focus of death magic; when Ellania squinted, she could see motes of amethyst dancing by the trillion as the energies of death wound down the tunnels. Ellathor darted a look down the passageway; withdrawing, he quickly described what he had seen to his sister and the Stonemage Xelathuria. To his horror, the army of undeath that had amassed far beneath the earth outnumbered them a dozen times over.

The Lumineth who had ventured into the Granthium Mountains had uncovered a catastrophe about to unfold. There was no time to secure reinforcements; they had but minutes left if they wanted to avert disaster. As they struck out in a blaze of light, Neferata's royal horde turned as one to meet them.

Alacrity was of the essence. With a sweeping hand motion, Ellania caught the attention of all Lumineth present and pressed two fingers against the aetherquartz gem in her helm, absorbing its latent power until her eyes glowed faint pink in the darkness. Her fellows followed suit. Leaping into the air over her brother's shoulder, the mage prodigy flung out a hand. Nothing came from it, but a second later, scintillating bolts of light exploded on the far side of the cavern, causing many of the Soulblight vampires to cover their eyes and hiss in protest. The skeletons ringing the cavern had no eyes to cover; at a dismissive gesture from Neferata, they turned as one and advanced, spears lowered, towards the intruders.

The Lumineth cut through them like a lance tip through mouldering bone. Formed up in a wedge, the Alarith advanced steadily in good order, hammers swinging to shatter skeletal ribcages and crush skulls with impressive accuracy until bone powder swirled thick in the air. Then a cadre of armoured wights closed in on the advancing spearhead. It was a manoeuvre no mortal force could have performed, but these undead were thrall to a single will; the Deathrattle soldiers moved aside like the pieces of a complex interlocking puzzle to let their elite brethren through. Xelathuria chanted the song of the high peaks, and the ground below the leading force of wights parted to form a narrow fissure, sending scores of undead tumbling to a rocky demise. But the march did not cease. Ten, twenty, thirty skeletons tumbled across the fissure, but some were swift enough to grab the other side, forming a bridge of bone across which the wights renewed their advance.

Within a matter of minutes, the way to Neferata and the realmgate dais at the heart of the cavern was blocked, the spearhead surrounded by concentric shieldwalls of Grave Guard all braced to take the impact of hammers and thrust their cursed blades back in reply. The Alarith advance slowed to a crawl. Their hammers were still shattering shields and breaking skulls, just at a far slower rate – and, ultimately, time was all Neferata needed.

Howling over the heads of the Deathrattle skeletons came the Scarlet Doyennes, a trio of vampiresses with murder glinting in their kohl-rimmed eyes. They were borne upon a strange conveyance of rock, metal and silk held aloft by a swarm of thrall-spirits all singing praise to their mistresses in the dialect of ancient Nehekhara. At once, Ellathor saw the danger they represented – though they looked pale and slender of limb, they would each be the equal of a dozen Lumineth. Even as he watched, one of the vampires coaxed the lifeblood from an unlucky aelven warrior in a stream of crimson droplets.

As their floating palanquin came in low, Ellathor vaulted high, planting one foot atop a stalagmite to backflip onto the morbid conveyance, his sword sweeping around in a decapitating arc. His target leant backwards with unnatural flexibility, the blade coming so close to her throat that it slashed the bejewelled choker from her neck. In the space of a single heartbeat, she had pulled a runic dagger and sunk it into Ellathor's leg. He fought back the intense pain, punching the pommel of his blade into the nearest vampire's throat even as she spoke a death-curse. Then one of the vampiresses met his gaze, and he felt his world fall away, dwindling to nothingness.

Seeing her brother in mortal danger, Ellania rose high, flinging bolts of pure and searing light across the cavern so that two struck each of the vampiric coven. However, in doing so, she had revealed her position. Neferata herself called across to her from the dais, and despite herself, Ellania turned to answer. It was a grave mistake. Neferata beckoned, and Ellania's blood answered the call. She was pulled bodily towards the Mortarch, her veins afire with agony. Spellcasting was out of the question; it was all she could do to stop her sudden and dramatic exsanguination. One lapse of concentration and her lifeblood would burst from her body.

The amethyst magic of ending swirled everywhere, dimming even the brilliance of aetherquartz. Nearby, the Alarith advance stopped entirely as a cloud of bats descended, screeching, from the stalactites high above to fall upon the tall-helmed aelves. While the skeletons were a foe well suited to the Lumineth's hammerblow assaults, the bats proved too fast, too agile, even for aelven reactions. They latched onto faces and necks with their needle fangs, causing the Stoneguard to drop their weapons in their attempts to claw the beasts free. Then came the ambush: a Terrorgheist hell-bat, dropping from the darkness of the ceiling to emit a blood-curdling howl. The sound was horrifically intense, killing several Alarith instantly.

Xelathuria cried out in dismay, shaping the stalagmites of the cavern's floor into jutting spears that shot up to impale the beast. Her fleshless foe was not slain, however. It hauled itself bodily from the spikes and lunged for her.

Calling out a word of power, the Stonemage opened another fissure – only to be consumed by it, falling in silence into its depths. Her Stoneguard gasped in shock. Could it be that she had lost control of her own incantation? A horrible moment of uncertainty passed, the chanting of Neferata's acolytes rising to a high pitch as the black disc of the dais began to pulse with a hideous purple light. The howl of the Shyish Nadir haunted the edge of hearing, and the arid scent of dry and lifeless desert filled the cavern, carried on a hot and stinging wind.

There came a sudden wrenching, grinding sound as the stony, glittering ore of the cavern's floor heaved upwards. A figure took shape there, golden and magnificent, its horned head that of an immortal longhorn, a massive maul in its hands. It was a Spirit of the Mountain – in fact, the very mountain in which the Lumineth fought. Cradled like an infant in one of its long, slender arms was Xelathuria, half dead with effort and curled in a foetal ball as she lent her magic to the soul of the mountain. Granthius, the aelementor was called, and its wrath burned hot. It swung its mighty hammer in a wide-reaching arc that smashed into Neferata's dread abyssal steed, hurling the Mortarch from her mount as the beast Nagadron exploded into a thousand fragments of bone.

The amethyst magic of the dais flickered and throbbed as Granthius strode forward, a tide of molten gold swilling around its cloven hooves. Wherever the undead tried to bar the aelementor's path, they were smashed aside. At a gesture from Neferata's ornate dagger, the skeleton warriors reformed and stood up to attack Granthius once more, but they could no more arrest its passage than a horde of stick insects could hold back a lion. The Terrorgheist swept in with a killing screech, claws extended, only to be met with a beam of searing golden light that pulsed from Granthius's forehead. This did not kill the beast so much as repel it, but that was enough. With a great rumbling roar, the Spirit of the Mountain brought its hammer two-handed in an overhead blow that smashed into the dais at the heart of the ritual.

With a shrill curse of outrage, the Mortarch of Blood thrust her hands towards the roof of the cavern before discorporating into a miasma of deathly energy. The runes she had inscribed in the cave ceiling before starting the ritual activated, and the entire roof collapsed, burying both aelf and undead under countless tonnes of rock. It was an act of surpassing spite, and one that would entomb the majority of those present for evermore.

MARCH OF THE MYRIAD

The cold war between the gods of Light and Death had been escalated massively by the Nighthaunt invasion in Hysh, then became a retributive campaign in the Ossiarch Empire. Now, with Nagash's ire raised, Teclis' strongholds in Ymetrica came under attack – not from a conventional force but from one steeped in magic.

The Blackpit Realmgate was a smudge of pitch on the pale foothills of the Ymetrican wilderness. Like so many other places abandoned after the Ocari Dara, it had been quarantined, forbidden for so long that the Lumineth avoided it out of habit rather than through conscious decision. Light bent around it, making it all but impossible to perceive – the Lumineth who had removed the realmgate from sight and mind had done a sterling job. Yet it existed still and was known, if not in Hysh, to those of Shyish who dwelt on the other side.

Now, on the eve of Nagash's counter-invasion, pale green lights began to emerge within the Blackpit's depths, each flickering pair emanating from the eye sockets of a ghastly death's head. The purpose of these lights, however, was not to illuminate but to instil fear. Out from that dark pit crawled the Null Myriad, bony fingers digging into Hysh's soil as they hauled themselves over the lip and formed up into echelons awaiting their master's command. Only when a thousand of these warriors had emerged did Arkhan the Black soar from the throat of the pit upon his dread abyssal Razarak. With him came winged Morghasts, and massive Gothizzar constructs that lumbered out of the realmgate on ramps of solid bone. The Null Myriad had come to Ymetrica in force, their Mortis Praetorian allies not far behind. Arkhan looked upon the assembled host and was pleased. For all their vision, the Lumineth still had blind spots waiting to be exploited.

The Ymetricans were far from unaware of the invasion; so in tune were they with the landscape itself that little happened in the peaks of that mountainous domain without their knowledge. They knew better than to attack the Null Myriad next to the Blackpit Realmgate, however, for there the energies of Shyish would be so strong that Arkhan would be at his most powerful. He had already broken through the protective wards around the site, burning them out with the sheer force of his dark magic. Instead, they faced the Null Myriad at altitude, where they knew the traditional phalanx-and-echelon tactics of the Ossiarch Empire would founder and the mastery of the Lumineth would allow them to turn the elements themselves against their foes.

At first, the plan seemed sound. The Ymetricans, led to battle by the Scinari Cathallar known as the Weeping Veil, lured their enemies into a valley that appeared to be surrounded by high peaks – but in fact had open paths leading into it. Obscured by folds in perception put there by the resident Stonemages to mislead such an incursion, these paths would be the perfect points from which to launch an ambush as the Null Myriad passed through to the Alarith shrines beyond. However, Arkhan, flying high upon the back of Razarak, saw through the arcane ruse moments before the trap was sprung. Instantly reacting as one to their master's telepathic orders, the Ossiarch soldiery began to retrace their steps even

ARKHAN THE BLACK

Of all the Mortarchs, Arkhan is the most trusted by his master Nagash. An exceptionally deadly sorcerer, his skill in the dark arts has only progressed over the course of his immortal tutelage under the Great Necromancer. It was Arkhan who undertook the millennial endeavour of assembling the Great Black Pyramid of Shyish, guiding uncounted skeletons in the thankless labour of stealing the grave-sand from the realm's edge in order to amass the raw materials required. Though it consumed his existence for centuries, it was a task that Arkhan completed. Now, with the Shyish Nadir ensuring that all dead things ultimately find their way to Nagashizzar, including the afterlives to which such souls are drawn, Arkhan has been given another assignment. He is to bring that same morbid fate to the Realm of Light, ensuring that the insult its aelven people paid to his master is avenged thricefold. With the skeletons of his former task remade as the Null Myriad, it is a duty he may well fulfil.

THE TEN PARADISES OF HYSH

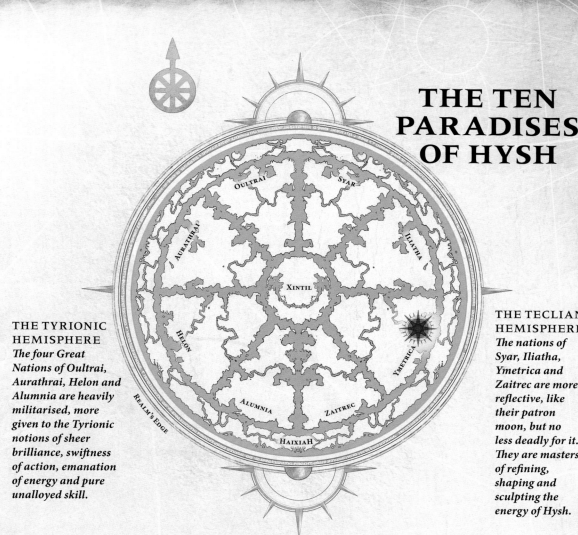

THE TYRIONIC HEMISPHERE
The four Great Nations of Oultrai, Aurathrai, Helon and Alumnia are heavily militarised, more given to the Tyrionic notions of sheer brilliance, swiftness of action, emanation of energy and pure unalloyed skill.

THE TECLIAN HEMISPHERE
The nations of Syar, Iliatha, Ymetrica and Zaitrec are more reflective, like their patron moon, but no less deadly for it. They are masters of refining, shaping and sculpting the energy of Hysh.

as the ambush was triggered, causing the aelves who had sought to surround them to overcommit. Instead, the Lumineth were drawn into the same valley that they had intended to use as a killing field. The Mortek Crawlers and Gothizzar Harvesters that had brought up the rear rained fire into the aelves before they could rectify their mistake. Sharpshooting Vanari archers, hidden amongst the rocks, fired arrows that struck home but did not fell the Ossiarch footsoldiers picking their way through the valley. Spearmen attacked from hidden bluffs and moss-veiled caves, but they were driven back, for the thwarted ambush had become a battle of attrition, which favoured their tireless foe. Even the Lumineth's magical attacks floundered. Where the Scinari mages loosed bolts of searing light into the Mortek Guard, they sputtered into nothing more than a faint glow. Explosions of killing light beaded and trickled from the armour of the Null Myriad like condensation and caused just as little harm – these constructs were created from the remains of the skeletons that had built the Black Pyramid; to them, baleful emanations were little more damaging than a hailstorm.

The despair welling up within the Lumineth at the sight of their adversaries' seeming invulnerability was quickly harnessed by the Weeping Veil. The Cathallar burned away the debilitating emotion, giving rise to a great cloud of psychoactive smoke which she sent drifting towards the Mortek Guard's ranks until it obscured them entirely. The march of the Ossiarchs wavered, for even the composite souls within their phylacteries were unable to fully resist the pall of concentrated misery and doubt. However, where a mortal force or even another Ossiarch legion would have been crippled by the onslaught of negative energies, it did not slow the Null Myriad for long. Arkhan the Black uttered an incantation as old as the realms themselves, and the Cathallar's shroud of anguish was lifted. Those baleful green lights appeared in the vale once more, burning amongst the horrific features of their owners, which remained unchanged as ever. The story was much the same in a dozen locations across the Ymetrican peaks. By the dimming of the Hyshian sunlight that signified nightfall, the mountains around the Blackpit Realmgate belonged to Arkhan the Black.

The Lumineth adapted quickly, however. Knowing that finesse attacks would simply rebound, and that even their magic was largely ineffective against the invaders, they called forth their artillery. Lightweight but able to pack a serious punch, elegant Starshard ballistas were set up at vantage points in the mountains that oversaw swathes of land around. The valleys below, still haunted by the dim green glow of the Null Myriad, were the perfect arenas for their crews' art. With one aelf selecting the right bolt for the job and another taking the shot, the weapons swiftly took a toll. At first, they used heavy-tipped ammunition to penetrate the thicker armour of the large constructs at the edges of the Ossiarch lines. Then, when the Mortisans moved to heal their creations, in doing so revealing their positions among the Bonereaper ranks, the crews smoothly switched to bolts weighted for greater range and accuracy, picking off the Ossiarch craftsmen. In this way, several Boneshapers were shot down before they could make their presence felt.

Small units of Alarith then attacked, skidding down the mountainsides to drive the Ossiarch line back, if only for a time. As they did so, Scinari mages used their magic to incinerate the remains of their foes, for the arcane resistance of the Null Myriad had little effect when the spell of their animation was broken. Moreover, with great sorrow, the Lumineth burned the bodies of their own dead. To do so without the proper funeral rites was a great taboo, but the

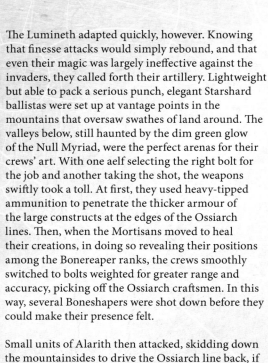

Lumineth had learnt from their campaign in Shyish, and they knew that if they were to win this new war, they would have to resort to extreme measures. The angst over such disrespect for the slain hung heavy in the air, as did the stench of burning bodies. Were it not for the Weeping Veil, it might have consumed the Realm-lords and pitched them into trauma. Yet the psyche-magic of the Cathallar kept them resolute, burning off the anguish of the living even as the flesh of their dead comrades turned to ash.

These acts of great sacrifice took their toll on the Ossiarchs. Where once their collector-constructs would have scooped up the remains of departed aelves and fallen Bonereapers alike, here they sifted through nothing but cinders, their giant rib-like harvester cages remaining empty. In time, even the most meagre remnants of bone could be reconstituted by talented Mortisans, but it was a far lengthier process and could not be undertaken on campaign. The Lumineth's tactics had put an end to that which the Bonereapers relied upon to fuel their inevitable conquests: the act of resurrection. When warriors fell, they would not return.

This was the critical turn of events that would see the Null Myriad's invasion go from one of grinding, relentless advancement to slow dissolution. The Lumineth fought with every ounce of agility and fluidity they could muster, pushing forward and falling back time and time again and leaving only smouldering ash in their wake.

When Sevireth, Lord of the Seventh Wind, came searing through the mountain vales at the head of a leaping, shouting spearhead of Hurakan warriors, the Realm-lords' campaign of slow starvation turned into a joyous, headlong assault. The arrows of the Hurakan archers were borne by their patron aelementor winds at such speeds that each missile decapitated its target on impact. Though the aelementiri were few in number, each shot was a vital kill, timed just as the main body of the Lumineth assault collapsed the shieldwalls of the Mortek Guard and ran amok in the ranks behind. Raising his bow, Sevireth sent fire-trailing bolts – each the length of a Mortek spear – smashing into the bestial skulls of the Gothizzar Harvesters beyond the front lines. Arkhan himself joined the fray, irate that his living fortress of bone was being picked apart. Those Lumineth who dared attack the liche found themselves aging at a horrific rate until their flesh turned to dust, but to Sevireth, the Curse of Years was of no consequence. The fiery wind-spirit sent forth a sandstorm of such violence that Arkhan was forced to fall back at the risk of being scoured to nothing by the hot, whipping gale.

A FATE POSTPONED

The Ossiarchs' defeat came slowly at first, and then all at once. With a cry, Arkhan swept his Null Myriad into a maelstrom of dark magic that transported them back through the Blackpit before his ritual to corrupt it was complete. The air was stained dark in their wake, the valleys swirling with what looked like a snowstorm but which was, in truth, the ash of burnt Ossiarch and Lumineth warriors mingled as one. Arkhan left his second, the Ossifector Xaramos, as a rearguard to drain the Lumineth of impetus by any means necessary, but next to Arkhan, he was a lesser threat. For a time, the Lumineth dared to hope that they had driven the Mortarch from Hysh for good.

Back in the relative safety of Shyish, Arkhan moved his forces from the far side of the Blackpit Realmgate to the Gates of Paradox, another portal to the Realm of Light that he had earmarked as a second staging point for an attack. The pace of the punishing journey he made across the harsh landscape of Shyish would have taxed a mortal army to its limit, but the dead know neither fatigue nor disillusionment. This time, he entered Hysh not in stable and well-defended Ymetrica but in the Desert of Ending in Haixiah.

Haixiah is the strangest and most magically saturated of all the Ten Paradises, for it forms the Realm's Edge itself. There, amongst shimmering, quartz-like vistas of solidified light, were the Gates of Paradox. These immense pillars of illumination linked Hysh to Shyish; between them was a great nothingness, for that specific region was both the cessation of light and the absence of shadow. It was a place of ending, redolent with the energies of the Realm of Death. Though not as potent as the Blackpit portal, it would suffice for Arkhan's ritual. Better yet, being so close to the edge of Hysh's Perimeter Inimical, no mortal army could advance upon it without risking total dissolution or transformation into something devoid of physicality. Only one who had braved the Realm's Edge and survived would dare to consider it a defensive strongpoint, and only Arkhan the Black had an army able to capitalise on it.

Constructed from skeletons that had once roamed the Perimeter Inimical of Shyish, the Null Myriad were inured to the baleful energies at the realms' extremities. For weeks, the Ossiarchs had laboured to populate the dune leading to the Gates of Paradox with a host of freshly made Mortek constructs. These were made of bone taken from those whom they had aggressively tithed in Shyish, alchemically treated to better survive the hazardous environment. Such was Arkhan's skill as a sorcerer that he needed no human sacrifice to power his rite of ending – just the undiluted magic of Hysh itself.

Visited by a vision of disaster sent upon shafts of moonlight by Celennar, the psychically linked Scinari Council learnt of Arkhan's fallback plan. Each meditating in their own spire, the High Scinari convened in wordless communion. They were faced with a dilemma – and a cruel one at that. Should they send a force into Haixiah, it would likely not return. It might not even reach its intended destination. Yet to ignore Arkhan's dire work would be to condemn the Teclian side of the Perimeter Inimical to a lingering, parasitic death and ultimately visit that same fate upon the edgeward reaches of the Ten Paradises nearest the realmgate. When the call to arms went out for this suicidal duty, there were none swift to embrace it – save one.

The question hung in the air: who would lead the forlorn hope into Haixiah, never to return? In answer, the Scinari Council was approached by a tall, radiant figure of pure light. Eltharion would lead the expedition – or rather his spirit would, for he had a vendetta against Arkhan the Black that had its origins in a former life.

The aelf and the liche had crossed their blades once before, long ago. In the cursed realm of Sylvania, the birthplace of Mannfred von Carstein, Eltharion had attempted to stop Arkhan the Black from resurrecting his master, Nagash, and precipitating the doom of the World-that-Was. On that fell day, Eltharion had been found wanting, and his mortal form had been turned to dust. Now, reborn in light in another life, another time, he had a second chance. His desire was fuelled not only by a sense of duty towards Hysh but by a cold need for vengeance.

Those Lumineth most faithful to Eltharion went with him, volunteering one and all to help their champion find a measure of peace and end the danger to their homelands, and indeed all the Mortal Realms. Wasting no time, they set off for the Realm's Edge, faces sombre and drawn. Few of them made it to their destination, for the intense magic of Haixiah turned their flesh to crystal, to light, to shimmering mirage. But the most stubborn pushed through, until finally they reached the perimeter beyond.

Yara Qu Wai narrowed his eyes against the intensity of the arcane forces that bleached the air across the Desert of Ending. Finally, the remains of their strike force neared the Realm's Edge. And there, atop the shining ridge that formed the horizon, were their targets.

To cross the Perimeter Inimical was to die. That much was known. The Windmage already felt cracks in his skin, the tiny shatterings of crystal that betrayed the fate in store for him. Six of his Hurakan brethren had been lost over the last month's gruelling march; passing through what they believed to be harmless shafts of light, they had been transmuted into inert glass statues of their former incarnations. Overnight, three more had been reduced to nothing more than odd, angular discolourations upon the sand, their bodies completely erased.

The Lumineth had not slept since then. Fatigue was setting in, and even the Alumnian veterans leading the expedition had stumbled one by one as they had made their way across iridescent dunes of geometrically perfect sand. Only the Light himself had kept his footing. His strides were metronomic and precise. Yara Qu Wai found himself thinking of the Lightning God's paladins, slowly reduced to creatures of mechanistic vengeance.

Perhaps half a mile ahead, the final dune loomed. Men of bone rendered tiny by distance already marched towards them, growing larger. Arkhan's minions, no doubt. Ahead, the Light of Eltharion had stopped, aetheric currents whipping around him. Yara Qu Wai summoned his wind-djinn and rose up the dune's gentle slope to meet the immortal commander, his Hurakan fellows and the Alumnian Vanari coming with him.

There atop the ridge, less than an arrow's flight away, were two immense pillars of raw Hyshian energy – the Gates of Paradox. It hurt to look at them. Already the scent of death was thick on the wind. Marching down that dune was an army of the dead, a glowing miasma of greenish energy flowing around them wherever they gathered in great numbers. Behind them, to one side of the realmgate portal, stood the liche.

~The moment is nigh,~ came Eltharion's voice in his head, archaic in accent but sure in tone. ~This, like all things, must end.~ The armoured apparition drew his blades, and charged.

'Hurakan! With me!' shouted Qu Wai. Riding his wind-djinn up the dune, he was joined by a score of Windchargers, each loosing arrows into the largest of the morbid constructs that marched amongst the enemy's bone-sculpted infantry. The Light had made his objectives clear at the outset, and Yara Qu Wai had every intention of furthering them. He called out to the legendary winds Garhael and Daramanth, sending the Hurakan aelementors forward to toss undead forms left and right. Qu Wai added his own gale to the cause. Amongst the Mortek battleline, a clear path was made, as if a river had been parted to expose the sandy bed beneath. Arkhan glowered at the end of it, staff raised as he stood in the saddle of his great deathless steed. The Hurakan surged forward, but Eltharion outdistanced even them, sprinting in a blur of light straight for his nemesis.

'A formless echo of revenge,' came the death-rattle voice of the liche. 'How pathetic.' Arkhan's image split and then split again until five Mortarch simulacra loomed atop the ridge, each atop its own dread abyssal steed. Eltharion answered with a lancing beam of light from his sword that seared into the central image, blasting it into glittering fractals. Qu Wai shouted a warning as the jaws of the leftmost image gaped impossibly wide, but it was too late; black tendrils shot from its maw to grasp at Eltharion's limbs. They passed straight through, for inside the armour there was no substance to grab. Vaulting free, Eltharion thrust the tip of the Celennari blade under a prism-like rock and flicked it aloft. Another beam shot from the aetherquartz on his helm, this time refracting through the prism rock to sear into the remaining simulacra. Three disappeared, the fourth falling from the saddle of its steed in an explosion that sent the beast reeling.

The Light of Eltharion charged in without breaking stride. Within seconds he was there, his twin blades thrusting forward to pierce the Mortarch's torso. Blindly, Arkhan's steed Razarak swiped out with a huge claw, but the beast could not hope to catch a warrior as swift as light itself. In darted the Fangsword, cutting deeper this time. Purple-black light spilled from the liche's wounds. Arkhan spat a dark curse and thrust out a hand to grasp at Eltharion's neck; it had been that same hand that had ended the aelf's former life. This time, the hand closed upon nothing but light. Eltharion's essence burned, and the liche withdrew his palsied claw, screaming as the magic that sustained his corporeality began to unravel. He staggered behind his mount towards the Gates of Paradox, hoping to interpose it between him and his nemesis, but it was no use: his foe was too nimble. Qu Wai sent a wind to keep Arkhan's warriors back as the Light drove the liche away from the realmgate, the aelf's blows unremitting. To the very top of the final dune the Mortarch was driven, to the very edge of Hysh, where even the laws of reality could be undone.

Then, with a final push, Eltharion cast his nemesis into pure nothingness. Howling, Razarak dived after him. There was a blinding explosion of light, and the last thing Yara Qu Wai ever knew was that the Mortarch and his steed were no more.

The surest path to enlightenment is to journey to its furthest limits and become one with its illuminating energies. Unfortunate, then, that this is also the surest path to bodily destruction.

- Neognosis Teclimentari

TABLEAU OF THE FATES

From Chamon's deep and glittering tunnels, the dark queen and her false kindred withdrew. A spiteful curse of ending she cast to bring the golden mountain low. Had that proud peak not taken aelementor form, its allies in aelfkind would never have seen the light again.

In grim Shyish the blood-king took his chance, for his rival the dark queen, still a parasite in Chamon's breast, was not there to stop him. So his legions marched upon her sovereign lands, even as her night-hunters and courtly agents claimed subtler victories in the blood-king's own territory. Such is the way of the vampire, for they are beings that can never truly rest.

Of the battle under jade skies, between radiant life-goddess and darksome blood-king, only one could hope to survive. It was a truth the vampire had foreseen, and in that admission, found a path to victory. Back to Shyish fled the dark one, his monstrous creations sacrificed upon the Everqueen's spear.

At Hysh's edge they fought, their blows driven by an enmity steeped in aeons. There, no mortal creature could have bested the Liche of Nagash. Yet the Light was no mortal, and death had little hold upon him. The Mortarch fell that day, and the Ten Paradises were freed from his ancient curse for evermore.

ACT III

A CLASH
OF GODS

FAKIR'S
WASTE

STADIUM
ILLUMINATOS

SYLL'ESSKAN
WASTES

THE LEAPS

GLORIANI'S
ECHO

THE LAST
PORTAL

THE BLEND

THALUIN
RECLAMATION

TEMPER'S
FLARE

XINTIL

EXTRAPOLATED
SPUR

THE GIRDLESEA

COAST OF LUCID DREAMS

DOOM OF
SPIRES

LOTHRIL RIVER

ILIATHA

VAROUR'S
LESSON

CEYLIAN
STORMBREAK

HANORI
SEAL

BREAKING
POINT

TOR
QULIAN

SHIMMERSEA

TOR
KITISE

LACOI'S
TRIUMPH

ARCH OF
MEN

FRACTAL
FJORDS

TOR
AMUN

COAST OF PRISMS

RUINS OF
AILLIANIS

CLASH OF
NATIONS

TOR
ILIDRET

LAKE
PERPENDICULAR

TOR
ELID

GLIMMERING INLETS

QUISLAI BRACE

REVELATIA

REVELATION DESERT

ALABASTER
CANALS

AROTH
STRONGPO

CYTHON'S
BITE

MOUNT
AVALENOR

CRAKENMAW
CHASM

MALANIA'S
LAMENT

TOURMALINE
SPIRES

HEL
CLASH

THE PILLAR
OF TRUTH

BLACKPIT
REALMGATE

HEDONIST'S
REVEL

THE CRUMBLING COAST

AVALENORIA

YMETRICA COREWARD

SCINTILLA FALLS

SETTLER'S GAIN

ELDOIR RANGE

THE GREAT
VINDICATION

VERTIGINOUS PEAKS

THE GIRDLESEA

GLIB
STRETCH

LOTHIL DELT

ELTHONDU

TOR
XILLION

THE
PIERCING
LAKES

SARATRAI
CHASM

ILARU JETTIES

SUNDRAKE
CREST

SELENI COAST

FALLEN
CYRIA

IL'DOSTILYA'S
FOLLY

GREAT DAIXO RIVER

TYRION'S
FLAW

RUINLIGHT SOUND

SHATTERING CLIFFS

DRAKSPINE PEAKS

CYRIAN
WASTES

MELUVANE

STOICAL
VAST

THE
NOTHINGS

SETTLER'S GAIN

*A shining beacon of civilisation,
Settler's Gain is a human city with
Lumineth mentors.*

CRYSTAL
CAVERNS

CELENNAR'S
GIFT

SEAPORT
MATAH

MOILA
VARDAN

UAIMH
WHIRLWAY

LUNEGLOW

ZAITREC

ISTRIN
ARCGATE

MER ZAIMETRICA

THE
BEAK

LECA
BEAC

MONCHILDRANI

CARAVANSERAI TRADE RO

CORRUPTED
CRATERS

YMETRICAN GEOSEGMENT

THE
BITE

TRANQUIL
PLAIN

THE
BROKEN
DELUGE

ZOROSTRAMARAN
DESERT

VERTIGINOUS PEAKS
The lair of a vicious Flesh-eater Court, these mountains are quarantined by all Lumineth.

LABYRINTH OF CLONES

TOR LIMINA

MER ILIMETRICA

YLTIPAI SVELD

YLVANI SEAL

THE BRAND ORIOUR

DEARTH INTRINSICA

ELTHRIAC BURN

YNTRIL COAST

THE BROKEN SHARDS

NEOQUANTIS COAST

FANGS OF ILLU-THAIN

UENTAL GRACE

BEL SARATHAIN

TOR PRINDIS

TOR GLIMRIS

SAROIR AFTERMATH

PALISADE FIELDS

KAIROS' RESURGENCE

UEL TAZALAR

CONTRARIAN RIVER

BEAMING DESERT

PHA'S GLORY

YMETRICAN VELDT

SCINTILLA GATE

THE FLOODED INLANDS

THE BATTLE OF THE GREAT FLOOD

YMETRICA

SETHAI'S SCAR

YRILI FISSURE

LUMINARIS SEA

DESERT OF ENDING

LUNAREST

THUNGUR LODGE

THE PIT OF CATHARTIA

TECLIAN LIGHTFALLS

THE SCOUR

SCHOLAR'S GIFT

DESERT OF FASTING

THE SHADRIAN CRISIS

RUINS OF EVERGLEAM

MITHRIS CLIFFS

YMETRICAN BARB

RIVER CATARAI

BAY OF TEETH

LÉIRGAETA WHIRLWAY (TO ULGU)

TO THE REALM'S EDGE →

BEL'SHADRIA

DOOMSTRETCH

ZOEC TRILL

TOPPLESPIRE

HAIXIAH

ZONQUIL'S SHORTCUT

SARIOUR PLATEAU

YDRIL'S CRATER

HARMONIOUS CHAIN

ELUI YMPRESSE

SUBLIMATION'S POINT

VALE OF KILLING TRUTH

THE TOPPLING OF THE ARCHES

ZENITHAL PLAINS

BLINDING RIVER

ALIXILA PLAIN

HYSH IN PERIL

The Ossiarch assault on Hysh cast a pall over the heart of Ymetrica. Though the Lumineth had thrown back the Shyishan invaders, the nightmare was soon to begin anew.

Again and again, the Lumineth met the Ossiarch Bonereapers on the field of battle, the sheer brilliance of the aelves matched against the relentlessness and grim artifice of their foes. The skies darkened over Ymetrica as hundreds of thousands of bats flocked from their caves, driven to frenzied bloodthirst by the influx of death magic. The mountains themselves began to shiver as if in horrified anticipation, their rocky flanks bleeding a thick crimson liquid as the air soured. Something vile and unnatural was coming, that much even the animals of the high peaks could sense.

Then, amid a scream of tortured magical energies, Nagash broke through the Blackpit portal, overpowering the wards and defences the Lumineth had begun to work around it. The vengeance of the Supreme Lord of the Undead was soon to be made manifest.

THE DESERT OF ENDING
The psychedelic crystal deserts near the Realm's Edge can transform a mortal to light alone.

DARKNESS DESCENDS

The air over the Ymetrican mountains shimmered with an aura of amethyst light as the energies of death coalesced around their master Nagash. Here the Great Necromancer's wrath would be felt most keenly of all, though if his ritual reached completion, all of Hysh would pay the price.

Above the yawning, rock-toothed abyss of the Blackpit Realmgate, the sky sickened fast. A riot of nauseating colours threaded through the gossamer clouds that drifted overhead. Traces of sour scent infected the air, the stink of corpse-rot mingling with the musky, arid smell of desert tombs. Birds and even insects fled on instinct, as they would before a storm. Yet it was nothing so natural as a seasonal tempest that was coming to the Ymetrican peaks: it was a sucking, lifeless void, and at the heart of that incipient disaster was a god.

A titan of deathly power burst from the Blackpit portal with a scream of triumph. Around the circumference of the pit, aelven warding runes burned with black fire, the symbols shrivelling and writhing as if in pain until they disappeared altogether. The godly figure rose up and rose again, a pall of dark energy playing about him like a thunderhead around a high peak as amethyst lightning crackled between his mantle of spine-like tendrils. The energies of Hysh dimmed as if afraid to touch him, the shadows crawling and slithering away from the baleful luminescence of the unquiet spirits that swirled about him and the macabre, human-skin grimoires that hovered within his reach. Already immense, the figure seemed to grow even larger as he cast hollow eyes across the mountainous terrain. Wherever his gaze fell, the Lumineth soldiers set to guard the portal withered and turned black. The survivors fell back in terror, bolting for mountain paths and hidden valleys in the hope of living to fight another day – for against such a foe, no mortal army could hope to prevail. Realm-lord falconers sent proud sun-eagles winging away to bring word to the greater Lumineth host. The deathly god twitched a talon the length of a sword; shrieking, the eagles burst into purple flame and turned to dust that swiftly dispersed on the wind.

Stooping, the skeletal monstrosity placed its bony hands upon the flank of the mountain and chanted words of power that would have seared the mind of any mortal to hear them. The stone beneath his touch began to shiver and crumble, cracks spreading at an alarming rate across the flank of the mountain as the rich, dark rock turned brittle and white. A circle of pure ending-magic spread out around the manifesting deity, the rock-crawlers and granite-

lizards caught in its field trembling as if in palsy before growing ancient in a matter of moments. Nagash had come to Hysh.

MARCHING TOWARDS DEATH

The Lumineth hosts that hailed from Ymetrica had been decimated in Praetoris some months before. Some had not yet made it back to the heartlands of the Great Nation they called home. Nigh unable to bear the horrible memories of their time in Shyish, the most part of the shining companies from the Teclian Vanguard had sought out the Elthondu Widows, who waded the Great Daixo River. There, they had hoped to extirpate their anguish with the aid of the strange emotive arts of the Cathallar sisterhood. But the moment that Nagash breached the wards of the Blackpit Realmgate, the sage magisters of Elthondu found their hearts racing as if a cold hand was squeezing them. They cried out as one, tears pouring down contorted faces as they shivered and spasmed in terror. A collective shudder ran through those Ymetricans who witnessed the Cathallars in their fugue state. That which had haunted their long, fraught nights had come to pass; they could feel it in their souls. *Avalenor*, said the seer-women. *Avalenor will tremble and fall.* Emotionally shattered as they were, the Ymetricans strapped on their armour once more and set out, this time with many of the Elthondu Widows at their side.

Word was sent, borne by messenger hawks and the fastest riders of the Vanari hosts, to the neighbouring nations of Zaitrec, Iliatha and Xintil. It was likely they were already too late, for if Nagash was truly walking Avalenor's flanks, he would have cemented his control over that region within days, not weeks. Yet the Lumineth had taught the citizens of the Shyish Innerlands – so recently under the heel of the Ossiarch Bonereapers – the value of hope, and they were keen to retain it for themselves, even if it were only a sliver of light amidst the darkness.

At first, the Lumineth companies made their way through the mountains at a slow but unrelenting pace. Now exhaustion was taking hold. By the express order of their commanders, their reserves of aetherquartz were to be held back for the conflict ahead, yet still, many an aelf absently ran their fingertips across brooches and gems of the invigorating substance or gave in to longing fantasies of letting its light burn through them. Already they could feel a weight of despair in their chests: they were too late to stop Nagash from succeeding where Arkhan had failed, and they were likely too few in number to overcome a force of animated corpses, let alone a fearsome army of Ossiarchs, whose very purpose was war and conquest. Their mastery of the magical arts seemed meagre indeed next to the skills of an immortal deity who had turned an entire realm inside out and sent his malevolence cascading across the cosmos. They were but insects before a giant, mortals before a god; they could no sooner stop the Great Necromancer than a leaf could stop a gale. In their hearts, only one hope remained.

That hope was Teclis and his brother, Tyrion. However, according to the Scinari, neither of the aelven gods were to be found in Hysh. There were rumours circulating amongst the wardens of Uhl-Gysh that Archaon the Everchosen himself had made an attack upon the Hidden Gloaming and that the worshippers of the imprisoned god Slaanesh had surged from Ulgu to attack that secret gaol. Word had it that Teclis, having struck his blow against the Realm of Death, had made haste to that twilight sub-realm to ensure they could not free the Dark Prince from the chains of paradox that bound him fast. As to Tyrion, none knew of his whereabouts. He had departed from the shrines of Alumnia on a singular quest, the nature of which he refused to disclose, though there were those amongst the Vanari that said he had made for the Pit of Cathartia in Ymetrica. So it was that in Hysh's hour of greatest need, the gods that called that realm home were absent.

It was Lyrior Uthralle who led the Vanari of Ymetrica in Tyrion's stead. At the Lord Regent's command, the Lumineth strongholds of Tor Amun, Tor Ilidreth and Tor Glimris were emptied, their phalanxes crossing Revelatia, closing over the Contrarian River and bridging the Scintilla Falls to reach the northern edge of the Vertiginous Peaks. From on high, they appeared as trickling streams of silver, blue and white that snaked around the terrain to climb into the highlands that stretched out around Mount Avalenor. Their target was easy to identify; high in the sky, beyond the Blackpit Realmgate, the air itself had turned dark and foul like an old bruise. To look upon the anomaly for too long was to see visions of numberless corpses and skeletal forms, leering and staring with empty sockets as the whispers of the dead filled the mind. Not one of the Lumineth gave voice to their fears. This was their home, the very lands that they had sworn solemn vows to defend, and even in the face of almost certain destruction, they would take no backward step.

When the aelves approached the site of the Blackpit, they beheld something even more disturbing: a globe of swirling, monochrome energy so large that it looked as if a small moon had settled over the portal. As the Lumineth grew closer, they saw that the sphere was formed not of amorphous magic, but of churning spectral forms. From it, a shrill cacophony was carried on the wind towards the aelves, a screeching chorus of anguish that sounded as though it had been ripped from a thousand ragged throats.

Lord Regent Uthralle was about to order that the horrific phenomenon be bombarded with the cleansing magic of Hysh when the Weeping Veil laid her hand on his arm, staying his command. The globe contained Lumineth souls: those aelves who had fallen in Shyish some weeks earlier. To destroy the globe would be to condemn them forever to a lightless purgatory. Nagash had used the aelves' reverence for the spirits of their own kind as a shield, and an effective one at that. It was with great sorrow and grim determination that the Lumineth marched onwards, seeking the architect of the pit's transformation. On the twelfth night, a messenger owl had brought word from the Ymetricans still in Shyish. The essence of Mount Avalenor itself, the Spirit of the Mountain who walked with stately grace at the head of the Shyish invasion force, was cracking and crumbling as if he were made from dried clay rather than impervious rock.

Ellania, returned from Chamon alongside the Alarith survivors of that ill-fated expedition, made the leap of logic first. She shared her suspicions with Ellathor before presenting them to Lord Regent Uthralle. If Avalenor's avatar was crumbling, she claimed, it was probable that the mountain itself was in dire peril – and likely from Nagash, for it would take no less a foe to bring down such a place of aeons-old power. The Lumineth host, already force-marching, broke into a measured run. No human army could have made such swift progress through the mountain paths, but sure-footed and dexterous even in their fatigue, the shining companies made good time.

As they made their way into Avalenoria proper, the Lumineth armies were confronted with a series of horrific sights. The aelementiri shrines that dotted the winding pathways were reduced to burnt-out ruins, the skins of their keepers and disciples draped upon jutting spars of wood or strange, tree-like structures of bone raised by the hideous arts of the Ossiarch Mortisans. It was a warning sign so clear that even a troggoth could have comprehended it, but it deterred the aelven hosts not at all. If anything, it hardened their resolve, for to see their kin so horribly mutilated lit a fire for vengeance within them.

The attacks had begun in the dead of night. The Ossiarch Bonereapers had invaded in force and barricaded the ancient trails leading to the peak of Mount Avalenor with fortresses of stolen bone. Those Alarith left behind to keep their mountain home safe had been slain to an aelf. In a hideous, ironic indignity, their bones had been stripped from their bodies and used to make walls to keep their brethren from avenging them whilst Nagash closed his grip on Ymetrica's stony heart.

The battles that raged along the mountain passes were even fiercer than the clashes in Praetoris where the Lumineth and the Ossiarchs had first matched their blades, for now the aelves of Hysh were driven by a deadly, desperate hatred. Many of the Alarith amongst their number fought with hearts rather than heads, for they could not bear to see their patron aelementors laid low by Nagash's dark arts, and the appalling treatment of their kinsmen was still burning at the forefront of their minds. The Vanari, however, kept their focus. They gathered the bodies of not only their fallen but also the Ossiarchs they had laid low, transferring them far from enemy lines via networks of Dawnriders. In doing so, they denied their foes the resource they needed in order to replenish their ranks and erect their defences.

It was a tactic that had already proved highly effective against the forces of both Horrek Venzai and Arkhan the Black. Indeed, the latter had been forced to withdraw to Haixiah in order to begin anew the creation of a lesser nadir. Left behind to fight a rearguard in his stead was the Ossifector Xaramos. Though the Mortisan proved a capable general and diplomat, binding even the deranged Flesh-eaters who dwelled amongst the Vertiginous Peaks to his cause, he was to find that the tithe of bone could be too rapacious even for the undead.

The Mortis Praetorians that had sculpted the upper peaks into a nightmare of flesh and bone ranged ever further afield to shore up their defences. At first, they raided the Lumineth strongholds set into the mountainsides, only to be repelled or, when successful, find the bones of the dead already incinerated and turned to white ash by Hyshian magic. The bone-scattered slopes were harvested to the last phalange, and the nests of Ymetrican sun-eagles yielded slim pickings.

As the days of conflict stretched on, the very fortresses that the Ossiarchs had raised against the Lumineth were cannibalised to create new Mortek Guard. Such was the skill of the Mortisan priesthood overseeing the tithe and its application that, for a time, they appeared so formidable that the Lumineth simply did not attack – it was not in the nature of the Hyshian aelves to risk the lives of their own when the chances of victory were slim. But it was in the Vertiginous Peaks that the Ossiarchs were to make their first true mistake – and, in doing so, give the exhausted Lumineth a small chance of making a successful assault.

The Bonereapers had long considered the Flesh-eaters of Ushoran to be something akin to peasants, despite their claims of monarchical grandeur. They were useful as shock troops and allies, by all means, but they were unpredictable, and if anything can be said to be anathema to the Ossiarch Empire, it is unpredictability. Arkhan had left the Ymetrican war effort in the hands of his second, the Ossifector Xaramos, abandoning that Great Nation to start a new ritual in Haixiah. He did so in the knowledge that Gorstane Mortevell, Abhorrant Archregent and Bright Emperor of the cursed Vertiginous Peaks, was a stalwart follower of Nagash and would likely yield to the bone-tithe if needed. The dedication that Mortevell showed to Nagash was that of the religious supplicant, and as the test of time was to prove, he would gladly sacrifice his followers in the name of the Great Necromancer. The Archregent would fight tooth and nail to defeat the Lumineth – quite literally, in fact. Yet with his focus on the battle against the aelves, the calculating liche had not accounted for the courts under Mortevell's rule.

At first, the tithe of Starfang Mont, domain of the Ghoul King Varshorn, was a simple enough matter. Though Varshorn did not worship Nagash, let alone with the crazed enthusiasm, he saw the Ossiarchs as stalwart allies and allowed his forces to take the vanguard in a dozen minor clashes against the Lumineth. During the first phases of the battle for Ymetrica, whilst Arkhan was still in command, Varshorn had fought alongside the Mortis Praetorians, despite the differences between them. He had forged an uneasy respect for Xaramos over the course of the Ravage of Elthondu, where the two undead forces had engineered the sack of a prosperous Lumineth river town. The Ossiarch's thoroughness, creativity and patience worked well alongside the sheer ferocity of Varshorn's court, and after a string of victories over the aelves across Ymetrica Coreward, the Ghoul King had even invited Xaramos to the victory feast – the Ossifector had attended but did not partake.

The Flesh-eaters of that domain were not short of bone; in fact, their lairs were littered with it. At that time, Varshorn was willing to provide for the greater war effort. As the Lumineth bled the Ossiarchs white, however, the dynamic began to change. Xaramos, growing increasingly desperate for bone with which to bolster his dwindling forces, ordered the tithing of his allies. The crude, morbid sculptures and structures of Varshorn's court were torn down and repurposed, the grandeur of the throne room – in truth, more akin to a charnel pit – denuded to such an extent that it was entirely barren of what the ghouls considered to be sumptuous finery and important symbols of their sovereignty.

Mere days later, the bones with which Varshorn and his ghouls had decorated their skin were also forfeit. Then the call came for the remains of those warriors who had fallen in battle to be relinquished. When Xaramos demanded a tithe of the ghouls themselves, Varshorn reached the limit of his patience. He refused the tithe outright, instead inviting the Ossifector to discuss the matter at a banquet. Once more, the Mortisan ventured forth to Starfang Mont; this time, however, he did so with deadly intent.

The Ossiarchs attacked the Flesh-eaters, resolved to take the tithe from their deluded erstwhile allies by force – though in their haste, they had failed to scout the peaks. The battle that followed was bitter, with no quarter asked or given. All bar the hardiest of Varshorn's court were cut down even as the Ossiarch enforcers were torn limb from limb. The battle hung in the balance until the Bonereapers found themselves assailed by Varshorn's shock troops: winged ghouls that he envisaged as noble Pegasus riders coming to his aid. The cannibal Flesh-eaters screamed in triumph as Varshorn led the final counter-attack, the magic of his crown ensuring his court fought to the last. The Ghoul King closed his talons around Xaramos's throat and ripped his head from his neck, crunching the delicate bones of his face between yellowed fangs.

The loss of Xaramos's leadership hit the Ossiarch war effort hard, but not as hard as the loss of his expertise in the arts of boneshaping. Though he realised it but dimly, Varshorn had struck a blow for freedom upon which the Lumineth were soon to capitalise.

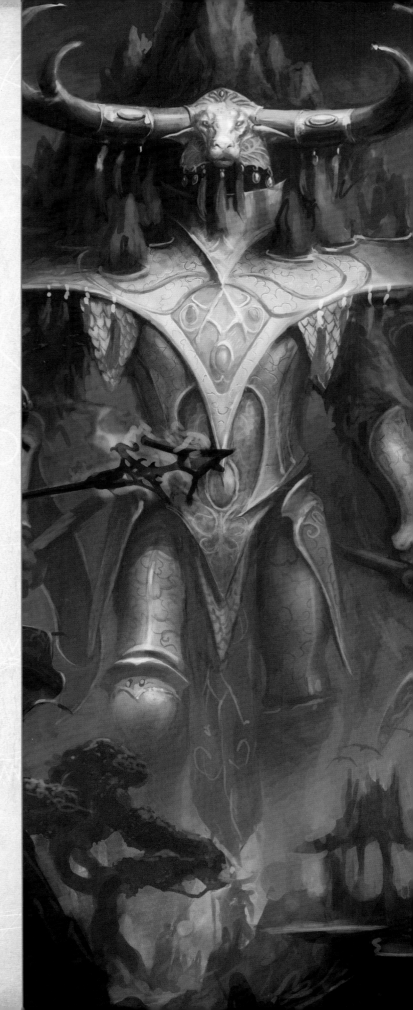

WAR ON THE PEAK

On marched the Lumineth assault on the peak of Mount Avalenor, their proud confidence replaced by grim determination. They would see Nagash defied and cast down, even if it cost them their lives – or worse, their immortal souls. In their hearts, they knew that only one force in the realms could save them.

The dark history of the realms had taught the Lumineth that the souls of those who stood against the Great Necromancer were likely forfeit. It was not in them to surrender, however; not since the Reinvention, when the Hyshian aelves had made the decision to act for the betterment of all instead of pursuing selfish ends. Here they would make their stand; in defeating Nagash, they hoped to end the curse of the Necroquake on all the Mortal Realms. Yet the closer they got to the summit of Mount Avalenor, the more they felt their resolve dwindle. The atmosphere was oppressive, the air stale and choking, as if it was thick with corpse dust. The Scinari Cathallars who sought to allay the waves of negative emotion emanating from the mountain found themselves aching from head to toe, their minds aflame with the effort of sublimating the currents of despair that were buffeting the shining companies on the approach. One after another, they collapsed to the floor, the spent aetherquartz carried in their ornately engraved bowls spilling down the scree slopes. Without their spiritual shield, the exhausted Lumineth found themselves giving in to the pall of despair that surrounded them. Gradually, the Vanari slowed as the sides of Mount Avalenor grew steeper; their tall bows and spears already made the climb difficult, even for a warrior in their prime, but now the ascent was made all but impossible by the deleterious energies of Nagash's curse. Even the stone itself was rendered brittle; seemingly sure handholds and outcrops crumbled whenever any significant weight was placed upon them.

Only the Alarith temples found the strength to carry on in force, perhaps lent a measure of stubbornness by the will of Avalenor itself and the might of aeons that had seen it survive even the Age of Chaos intact. The Stonemages reminded their kin that the mountain's endurance was limitless, and that whilst it stood, they too would stand in its defence. The truth of that notion wavered when scouts climbed onto a precipitous plateau on the shoulders of the mountain and saw a herd of pallid and emaciated Ymetrican Longhorns. The totemic beast of the Alarith temple owing to its imperviousness to disease and the elements, the Longhorn dies only when slain by a chance occurrence or in violence; left in peace, it is effectively immortal. Here, though, the creatures were sickening badly. They moaned and stumbled, their ribcages stark against famine-ravaged skin. It was a kindness, said the Stonemage Illitar, to put an end to their suffering. Their hearts filled with profound sorrow, the Alarith took their hammers to the foreheads of the blighted beasts. The poor creatures did not resist; instead, they looked up almost gratefully with their sad, deep eyes as the killing blows descended. Illitar ground her teeth at the sight, hatred giving her a new surge of energy.

Though it pained the Alarith to do so, they agreed with the Vanari leaders that they would forge ahead and disrupt Nagash's plan as best they could until the main body of the assault arrived. The next stage of the climb seemed to melt away for the aelementiri, for their wrath was burning hot and they were naturally adept at navigating mountains. There were whispers amongst the Scinari that the Alarith's rage at the destruction of their sacred lands was colouring their vision, and that they were heading into a trap, but there were no Cathallars still conscious to take the edge off their fury and restore their clarity of thought.

The Alarith climbed on. Set against Nagash on their own, they knew it would not be long before they were found wanting. As the aelementiri ascended, they called out into the winds that howled, tortured and terrified, through the mountains. Their message was borne from one wind to another, passed from mountain blizzard to flatland hurricane to storm at sea. Soon enough, the seventy-seven winds of the Great Nations heard the call, and their representatives, knowing how dire the hour was, made haste to Ymetrica as only a raging gale can.

It was the wind-borne children of Helon who reached Mount Avalenor first, for the foremost among them – the legendary trickster Harantio the Galerider – had already sensed the claw of Nagash stretching across the land. As the Alarith scaled the upper slopes, they found their handholds crumbling and the Tohnasai trees tearing away in clods of ashen rock, but whenever the aelves slipped or faltered, the winds of Helon would catch them and push them back to the rock face so that they might continue. The Alarith would fight that day with the Hurakan by their side. Better yet, the Hurakan were not the only force to have descended to their aid. There was a shimmer in the sky, and everything changed…

The sky screamed. The stony ground shuddered. Stale black gore drifted from a vortex of death magic that swirled around the peak of Mount Avalenor like a dark crown. Here was the great sacrifice Nagash needed to power his theft: not a mortal soul but that of a living mountain. Its end would be enough; that much Hysh itself knew, and had spoken through the wisdom of Celennar. If Avalenor died, what other peak could hope to survive?

Teclis narrowed his eyes against the whipping wind as he descended like a spear hurled from the vaults of heaven. He pierced the storm of deathly energies around the peak, magic funnelling into a cyclone around him. He did not need the witch-sight to pick out the monstrosity within.

Lit from below by amethyst light, Nagash was the stuff of nightmares given gargantuan form.

'AND SO YOU COME AT LAST.' The God of Undeath spoke without turning, hands still buried in the stone of Avalenor as if the mountain were made of clay.

'You can stop all this, even now,' said Teclis. 'It will not go well for you otherwise.'

'EVERYTHING BUT NAGASH HIMSELF MUST END.' The skeletal figure turned, his eyes blazing emerald green against the purplish pall of deathly energy. 'EVEN YOU, GODLING.'

'True, I feel. Yet I have a legacy in place, and it will not be you who brings about my demise. Was it not aelven magic from which you stole your power when you were little more than a fratricidal priest?'

'YOU SPEAK OF FRATRICIDE,' boomed Nagash, 'YOU, WHOSE MACHINATIONS DOOMED YOUR BROTHER IN A FORMER LIFE AND BLINDED HIM IN THIS ONE. PERHAPS THERE IS A REASON HE IS NOT HERE TO FIGHT ALONGSIDE YOU.'

'My brother fights in his own way,' said Teclis, 'against a foe far deadlier than you.'

'THERE IS NO SUCH BEING.' Nagash pulled his skeletal claws from the peak of the mountain and spoke a word of power, a trio of purple suns blazing into life around each of his wrists. He hurled them at Teclis, the malevolent orbs forming a deathly meteor shower that blazed towards him. They hit him with full force.

Suddenly, the Mage God was on the other side of the peak, framed by a nimbus of moonlight with Celennar spreading their wings behind him.

'In that,' said Teclis, 'you are quite wrong.'

The duel atop Mount Avalenor was a clash of titans, an epic battle of sorcery and willpower fought on the astral as much as the physical plane. The tale of how it unfolded was to echo across the history of the realms; in the future, scholars would claim that the battle had been inevitable ever since the first grain of grave-sand was gathered for Nagash's Great Black Pyramid. Perhaps both Teclis and Nagash knew this on some level; even when the two had been ostensible allies in the Pantheon of Order, both had dwelt long on the day that they would test their sorcerous might against one another. Since then, their power had only swelled, and here, on the peak of Mount Avalenor, it was to be tested as never before.

Celennar was first to strike. Hysh itself had suffered greatly at the hands of Nagash, and the realm's true moon would abide it no longer. A series of sliding, mellifluous chords issued from the sphinx's impassive mask, the melody winding around the peak to drown out all other noise. It was the music of the spheres, the most profound sound in the cosmos, and even the greatest words of power could not be spoken against it. Without a voice, a human sorcerer could not incant a great part of their spells, whether they be a simple hedge wizard or conjurer supreme.

Watch this exchange unfold, thought Teclis. It was a message he had imparted to thousands of students over the aeons. *Watch, reflect, countermand, and then, when the answer reveals itself to you, kill.*

Wordlessly, Nagash brought the tips of his talons together as if grasping a priceless relic. As he did so, a cage of glowing skeletal limbs appeared around Celennar, a thousand bony hands each clamping upon the forearm of another to make a lattice that trapped the moon-spirit entirely. The osseous globe began to contract as the spectral limbs scrabbled to grasp each other tighter, closer, harder, the whole prison in danger of crushing Celennar's physical form. In defence, the lunasphinx blazed with multicoloured light, shimmering waves of power emanating from its body. Though many of the skeletal arms burned to nothingness before the cleansing rays, there were always more to replace them, and these scrabbled all the more frantically to close the gaps in the lattice. The moon-spirit's wings were forced close to its flanks as the cage continued to shrink, and the hands began to rip into their prisoner's feathers and flesh. The beautiful music that had flowed from the moon-spirit fell apart into a thousand wracking sobs.

Nagash's hollow eyes blazed with amethyst light. He lashed out with the staff Alakanash and a roaring lance of purple flame shot towards the caged Celennar. With a thought, Teclis sent a wave of banishing magic to repulse it – but not without a deafening boom of redirected energy, just as Nagash had planned. Teclis threw up a shield of force to protect himself, but Celennar, enveloped by the constricting sphere, was blasted away as if struck by a battering ram. There was a shrill cry, a change in air pressure, and Teclis' ears popped as the aelementor retreated to the true moon.

With the Shyish Nadir empowering him from afar, Nagash was unstoppable. The skeletal tyrant loosed a stream of harsh syllables that curdled the air around his fleshless maw. Teclis felt, for a moment, an invisible hand closing around his neck. In his mind's eye, he saw his body convulsing as a swarm of carrion beetles devoured him from the inside out. Black sand poured into his mouth in such profusion that his slender form split open and burst like an overfilled sack. Coils of death magic wrapped around him, dragging him into an all-consuming darkness. He drowned in a sea of bone, fleshless fingers pulling him under. At the same time, he was immolated by an ancient sun ringed by a purple corona, crushed under the weight of millennia to nothing more than dust. Over and over, the barrage of nightmarish images battered his mind. He knew, in his heart, that to give in to the fear engendered by even one of them would be to make it real.

Teeth gritted, sweat beading on his skin, Teclis channelled the inner calm that had seen him last the aeons. He let the dark tides wash away from him like water from a marble obelisk. Suddenly, a brilliant light shone from him, piercing the pall of negative energy that swirled around his foe. Servant spirits that had been enslaved to Nagash for time immemorial discorporated as the beams of light touched them; they were not sent shrieking back to the Realm of Death but banished forever. All at once, the books orbiting the Great Necromancer – those unholy tomes that had been the stepping stones in Nagash's apotheosis – burst into white flame.

The Death God gave vent to a mind-splitting scream, a sound so vile that it cracked the mountainside beneath him. Avalanches cascaded down onto the battle far below, the weakened flanks of the great mountain falling apart with horrible ease. Teclis was forced to clasp his hands over his ears, feeling sticky blood seep between his fingers. The hideous noise threatened to rend his thoughts apart like gauntleted hands tearing through cobwebs. Putting fear from his mind, he brought a sphere of light into being around him and another around Nagash, sealing out the dark magic that raged around the peak and silencing the banshee scream of the Great Necromancer. Teclis squeezed his eyes shut, channelled the zenithal power that he had spent so long studying, and translocated. Suddenly, the dying mountains of Avalenoria were gone; all that surrounded Teclis and his nemesis were stars – and distant ones at that. From here, from the absolute peace of the void, a soul could open a gate, show the way, illuminate a path. The eyes of the ancient goddess-idol atop his staff seemed to find his. Watch, reflect, learn…

There was a sound like a thunderclap. Nagash had magically translocated from the sphere that had contained him into Teclis's own forcefield, his deathly stink filling it like the smoke from a crematorium. A monstrous being who made Teclis look child-sized by comparison, Nagash laughed as he swung Zefet-nebtar, the ancient blade causing reality itself to weep dark tears in its passing. Teclis parried with his own blade, the finest Syari smiths could make, but his strength was pitiful in comparison, and so the tyrant's sword came on. Only when he raised his lunar staff, locking the black blade of Nagash less than a foot from his forehead, was the force of the blow arrested. He could feel his skin shrivelling and flaking at the proximity of the deathly artefact.

No, said Teclis. Beams of pure Hyshian magic shot from his eyes, burning into Nagash's collarbone. They would have bored through the thickest fortress wall, melted even the Everchosen's hellforged plate. Yet here they did little more than scorch. The Great Necromancer brought his staff around, knocking Teclis' blade from his grasp. A mocking laugh echoed around the sphere of force as the stave thudded into the Archmage's ribs, and Teclis felt stabs of pain as the energies of the Shyish Nadir spilled into his essence and began to unmake him from the inside out. He coughed blood, the scarlet liquid glowing as it spattered his sleeve. In a flash, the spell of translocation was broken and the two were back atop Mount Avalenor, the din of battle rising to meet them. Teclis saw a glimmer of light from below – and took hope.

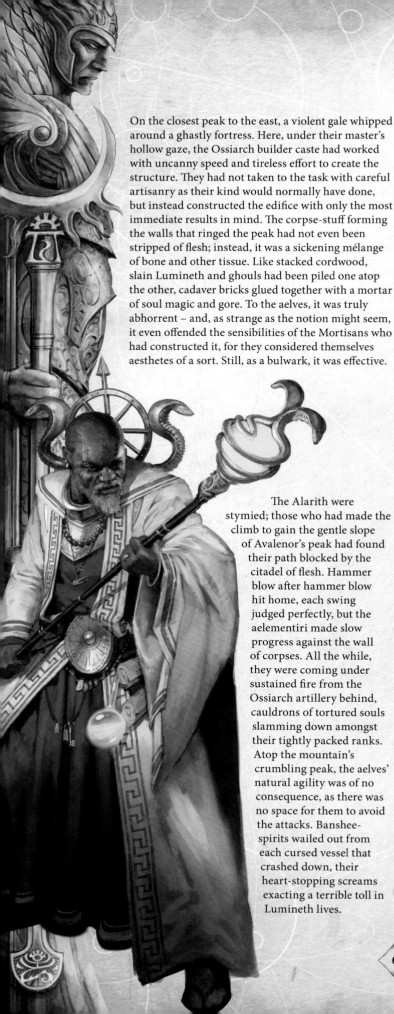

On the closest peak to the east, a violent gale whipped around a ghastly fortress. Here, under their master's hollow gaze, the Ossiarch builder caste had worked with uncanny speed and tireless effort to create the structure. They had not taken to the task with careful artisanry as their kind would normally have done, but instead constructed the edifice with only the most immediate results in mind. The corpse-stuff forming the walls that ringed the peak had not even been stripped of flesh; instead, it was a sickening mélange of bone and other tissue. Like stacked cordwood, slain Lumineth and ghouls had been piled one atop the other, cadaver bricks glued together with a mortar of soul magic and gore. To the aelves, it was truly abhorrent – and, as strange as the notion might seem, it even offended the sensibilities of the Mortisans who had constructed it, for they considered themselves aesthetes of a sort. Still, as a bulwark, it was effective.

The Alarith were stymied; those who had made the climb to gain the gentle slope of Avalenor's peak had found their path blocked by the citadel of flesh. Hammer blow after hammer blow hit home, each swing judged perfectly, but the aelementiri made slow progress against the wall of corpses. All the while, they were coming under sustained fire from the Ossiarch artillery behind, cauldrons of tortured souls slamming down amongst their tightly packed ranks. Atop the mountain's crumbling peak, the aelves' natural agility was of no consequence, as there was no space for them to avoid the attacks. Banshee-spirits wailed out from each cursed vessel that crashed down, their heart-stopping screams exacting a terrible toll in Lumineth lives.

Then, a hollow howling could be heard over the deadly shrieks, before it drowned them out entirely. The Hurakan Spirits of the Wind, summoned to war by the Alarith, had arrived. The aelementors swept away the banshees and even caught incoming projectiles in mid-air before casting them down the side of the mountain. The living gales swept around the peaks, hoping to seize the foes of the Lumineth and hurl them to their doom on the rocks below, but the Bonereapers were ready for them. Utilising their dark arts, the Mortisans fused their feet to the ramparts of the corpse-wall so they could not be dislodged. The howling of the wind took on a note of frustration, and in the din of battle, there were few who noticed that the sound was answered by wolf-like baying from the lower peaks.

Atop the walls of the fortress, richly dressed Mortisans shouted against the winds, their dolorous rites channelling long-stored power to their master Nagash as the gods of Light and Death duelled high above them. One after another, they collapsed, their souls drained entirely so that the Great Necromancer could gain an edge. Those who still stood were found by the arrows of the Hurakan wind-spirits, their lethal shafts twisting this way and that to bypass the grisly battlements. The Ossiarchs were concentrating only on defence. If the Lumineth could maintain the aggression of their assault, there was hope that they would break the invaders and leave Nagash with no physical presence on top of Mount Avalenor save his own. With the two gods in a deadlock, even mortal warriors could tip the scales.

Bridges of light cut through the air, summoned into being by Scinari who had levitated up the sides of the nearby peaks at Teclis' earlier insistence. A dozen shimmering planes of force appeared, then a dozen more. They were translucent and thin, but they were as solid as any rock-hewn causeway. Across them strode the Spirits of the Mountain that hailed from the other peaks of the same great range, the avatars of mountains that had stood alongside Avalenor for epochs. From on high, miasmas of amethyst energy floated down to discorporate three of the light-bridges, sending aelementors that were mid crossing tumbling silently through the air. Most of them found the sides of Avalenor, their long, sharp-hooved legs propelling them easily up the steep slopes.

They were not alone in scaling the peak. Up from the valleys came a pallid tide of ghouls, scrambling on all fours towards the crumbling summit of Mount Avalenor, the Archregent Mortevell at their head. Their unearthly screams echoed from the far mountains as madness given voice. To the Flesh-eaters, these were the clarion trumpet calls of a heroic charge against false angels, but to the Lumineth, they were tragic and daunting all at once. To the Scinari on the nearby peaks they looked like an infestation of white spiders boiling up from their nest, yet to the Alarith atop Avalenor, they were all too vivid a threat. In a wave of unclean flesh, they hurled themselves against the Spirits of the Mountain that were making for the Ossiarch fortress high above. Each sweep of the great hammers wielded by the aelementors sent a clutch of the creatures tumbling to their doom; each blast of geomantic energy from between the horns of their ritual masks incinerated half a dozen of the things mid-leap. Mortevell himself climbed, simian-swift, onto the shoulders of one of the mountain spirits and tore his mask from his head, causing the aelementor to crumble. Then the magic of Harantio the Galerider and his fellow Windmages, each riding the winds around the peak, caught Mortevell and hurled him screaming from the mountainside.

Were the Deadwatch of Starfang Mont part of the same assault, perhaps the Flesh-eaters would have tipped the balance, toppling the aelementors through sheer weight of numbers. Instead, the great war-spirits strode on, shrugging off the frenzied ghouls still hanging from their limbs, and took their immense two-handed mauls to the walls of the Ossiarch fortress that crowned Mount Avalenor. Though durable enough to hold back the main Alarith assault, the Ossiarchs' stronghold finally began to crumble; here were mountains given form, and they struck with irresistible force. As they did so, the Mortisans on the ramparts still funnelling power to Nagash were flung from the peak in a storm of body parts and splintered bone.

As the Ossiarch reserve filled each breach with a shieldwall of skeletal bodies, there was a blaze of light from six of the peaks opposite. It was so bright that the troglodytic Flesh-eaters shrank back with their claws over their eyes. The light intensified, dazzling even the Lumineth, before becoming a set of coherent beams that scorched their way through the twilight. Across the far side of the valley were six wheeled contraptions of human construction, each an array of focusing lenses – not glass, as in a telescope, but aetherquartz. Behind them was a shimmering portal, the spires of Settler's Gain just visible beyond it. Beyond the peaks themselves, or rather shining between them, was Celennar. The moon blazed

brighter than ever, nearly as bright as Hysh itself seen from the other realms. At the strident calls of the master mage Arcobalde Lazerne, the light of the true moon was carefully focused through the engines the humans called the Greater Luminarks of Xintil. Six searing lances of lunar energy sliced the air. Banishing the gloom, they struck Nagash in his torso, his waist, even his fleshless face as he fought Teclis above the peak.

It was all the opportunity Teclis needed; indeed, it was one he had put in motion at the very founding of Settler's Gain. The Xintillian light-engine *Beacon of Intellect* moved along the pass to channel the light of the distant Tower of Prios, just visible glimmering in the gap between two peaks. Blazing white, the Luminark's lenses focused the light of that far-off aetherquartz citadel into a deadly lance of energy that bored into Nagash's skull. Smiling in triumph, Teclis called forth the residual energy in each aetherquartz gem worn by every Lumineth present, a thousand tiny beams converging upon the Great Necromancer. With his mortal foe blind and reeling, Teclis called upon those same beams of energy and twisted them into chains of light. Just as he and his fellow aelf gods had bound Slaanesh in ages past, he bound Nagash, forcing the Death God down and down again until he was lashed to the peak of Mount Avalenor. Wading through the Ossiarch phalanxes that were rushing to protect their master came the massed aelementors of Ymetrica's mountains, each footfall crushing a bone automaton as they gained the peak. They raised their great hammers high and brought them down with the strength of ages to shatter Nagash's bones. Again and again the mountain spirits struck; trapped by Teclis' magical bindings, the Great Necromancer could not resist them. A god was broken that day, his physical form shattered and pulverised. Some amongst the Lumineth claimed to see a black shape, amorphous and strange, escape the prison of light to fly north in the direction of the Blackpit.

Glowing bright with power, Teclis pulled upon the cords of light that had bound Nagash and plucked the aetherquartz lenses from the distant Luminarks that were channelling them, hurling the discs high into the sky one after another so that they formed an artificial constellation. With their Ossiarch foes stunned into torpid inactivity by the destruction of their master, the Lumineth watched in rapt attention as the magical lenses were set in the firmament above Hysh. Seen from the cosmos, the radiant discs formed a pictogram – Danathroir, the rune of banishment and sanctity. In that instant, with Nagash exorcised and the light of Hysh blazing bright across the Mortal Realms, the lingering, deathly curse of the Necroquake was broken forever.

'Ultimately, life conquers all. Death is but another part of the cycle. As the rune Quul teaches us, it is both prelude and epilogue to the story of each living thing – as one thing withers, another blossoms in its place. This is a noble truth, for all that the Father of Plagues would seek to corrupt it, and for all that these human champions of industry would try and choke it. Life will abide, as I have. Then, when the time is ripe, it will thrive over all else.'

- Alarielle, the Everqueen

*A*n astral mirror shimmered in the void, a godly figure hovering cross-legged before it. To Teclis, the void was a place of meditation and reflection, and other than the Archmage's own breathing, the silence was total. He had summoned a twin astral mirror in the lush vegetation of Verdia in Ghyran, a medium through which Alarielle could speak to him, and now he had only to wait.

Teclis had fashioned a spherical garden of sorts around himself, the foliage made of semi-substantial light. He had long practised putting others at ease by presenting them with the things they expected to see. Make that concession, and they were more biddable – it was true even for his fellow gods.

A flash of memory came to him: a skeletal visage looming down. The memory of Nagash appearing before him inside his sphere of protection was difficult to dismiss. The hideous apparition had burst into his arcane sanctum with shocking ease.

He concentrated on the majestic female figure coalescing in the mirror before him, burning the haunting vision from his mind's eye with the light of reason. Alarielle was impressive beyond imagining – and stern. A true goddess; not some distant, abstract power, but one that would fight the forces of darkness with everything she had.

This time, at least.

'You realise what you have done, brother,' said the goddess. Her almond eyes were the deep green of a life-giving pool, hypnotising in their intensity.

'I understand the ramifications of my success, yes,' replied Teclis.

'You comprehend every aspect of them, and still you consider it worthwhile?'

'Why should I not?'

'It was a costly victory, and not just for Hysh. Nagash is not a forgiving god. He will work his vengeance, no matter how long it takes.'

'From his lair in Shyish, perhaps. I have bound him there, confining the spider to his web. He will not trouble the other realms for a long time.'

'Are you sure of that?'

Teclis did not deign to reply. 'Your old paramour and I thought it wise to lift the cold hand of death from the realms. Do you disagree?'

'It was necessary, as sure as spring follows winter. To achieve it so suddenly, however—'

'—was necessary, at the time,' insisted Teclis.

'There will be a backlash.'

'Of hope? Of progress? Or perhaps of enlightenment?'

'Of life,' she said simply, her crystal-green eyes seeming to draw him in. 'Life follows death, just as death follows life. And so the wheel turns.'

'Then you should thank me, should you not?'

'The realms will thank you, of that I am sure. Your pact with them has become stronger than ever. The same might not be said of their denizens.'

Silence stretched between the two gods, the cold of the void leeching away any former warmth.

'It was pride, of course, that was the chink in his armour,' said Teclis. His thoughts were drawn, like driftwood to a whirlpool, back to Nagash; they returned there far more often than the Archmage would like to admit. 'He thought he could defeat Hysh itself, banish the moon-spirit with a wave of his hand. Just as well. He had to think Celennar neutralised, to be blind to the true power of Hysh, just as he had to consider the artifice of the humans to be beneath him.' He inclined his head, just a little. 'There, I might have helped.'

'How lucky for us all that you Lumineth have so completely overcome your own pride.'

'Indeed,' said Teclis, nodding as he stared out at distant Azyr.

Alarielle shook her head. He was being deliberately obtuse, of course, and he took a wry pleasure in her exasperation, but he did not let a flicker of amusement show.

'And who do you think it was that lent you serenity at the critical moment?' said Alarielle, eventually. 'Who do you think looked out from the eyes of Lileath in her place atop the lunar staff I gave you myself, in a world long past?'

'It was… useful,' admitted Teclis. He smiled, just a little. 'And, I will admit, it was likely necessary.'

A sense of harmony settled upon him, the light-flora around him blooming and unfolding to become all the more beautiful.

'The beauty and strength of such unity might slowly return to the realms,' said Alarielle, reading his thoughts.

'Not yet, I fear,' he said. 'We have taken a great step, this day, and won a signal battle against the Nehekharan. Yet the war against the greater darkness remains to be fought.'

It was Alarielle, then, who tipped her head. 'I have more ways to fight them than you realise.'

'Then let us go forward together,' said Teclis, locking eyes with her once more. He heard a thin, echoing scream in the void and found his gaze drawn to the distant glimmer of Uhl-Gysh. 'Together, there is nothing our pantheon cannot achieve.'

'Let us hope that you are right,' said Alarielle. 'And if we are found wanting, let us hope that the realms themselves will heal from their wounds. Until next time, old friend.'

She reached out, touched delicate fingertips to the rippling surface of the mirror, and was gone.

'To pluck at the threads of destiny, to manipulate the skein and sew the tapestry of fate; this has always been the way of the aelven races. Their admirers say it is the legacy of those who live to see centuries pass by, and perhaps there is truth in that. Yet longevity does not grant omniscience. Not even the immortal can make that claim. Do not come to the notice of the aelves, my students. That way you may one day know peace.'

- Arcobalde Lazerne of the Xintil War-magi

THE RULES

BROKEN REALMS

This section of *Broken Realms: Teclis* contains exciting new rules for open and narrative play games. You can use the rules in this section to recreate the battles that were fought between the forces of Teclis and Nagash as they struggled for supremacy in the Mortal Realms.

CAMPAIGN RULES (pg 71)
This section includes a set of rules that allow you to link together the battleplans in this book, so that the result of each battle has an impact on the subsequent battles.

STREETS OF DEATH (pg 72)
This section includes rules that allow you to represent the challenges of fighting battles in the cities of the Mortal Realms.

REALMS OF BATTLE (pg 73-75)
This section includes Realmsphere Magic, Realmscape Features, Realm Commands and Realm

Artefacts rules that allow you to fight battles set in the locations described in the narrative section of the book. These rules have been designed for open and narrative play.

BATTLEPLANS (pg 76-86)
This section includes new battleplans that allow you to recreate the pivotal battles described in the narrative section of the book.

CAMPAIGN RULES

This book includes six battleplans, each based on a critical battle that was part of the campaign fought between the Lumineth Realm-lords and Nagash. The rules on this page allow you to play a series of linked games that recreates the events of the entire campaign leading up to Nagash's duel with Teclis.

THE ARMIES

This campaign is fought between two players. One player is the Teclis player and the other player is the Nagash player. The Teclis player must be able to field the following armies from the battleplans on pages 76-86:

- **Storm of Gheists:** Settler's Gain Army
- **Across the Plains:** Lumineth Realm-lords Army
- **The Reality Sores:** Maggotkin of Nurgle Army
- **All That Glitters:** Kharadron Overlords Army
- **A Fate Postponed:** Lumineth Realm-lords Army
- **A Clash of Gods:** Teclis' Army

The Nagash player must be able to field the following armies:

- **Storm of Gheists:** Nighthaunt Army
- **Across the Plains:** Stalliarch Lords Army
- **The Reality Sores:** Legion of Night Army
- **All That Glitters:** Legion of Blood Army
- **A Fate Postponed:** Null Myriad Army
- **A Clash of Gods:** Nagash's Army

THE BATTLES

The players must fight each battle in the order in which they appear in this book.

CONSEQUENCES OF BATTLE

Any named characters that are slain in a battle are assumed to have been hurt but not killed, and will be fully recovered in time for the next battle. This aside, the result of an earlier battle may have an impact on subsequent battles that are fought, as explained below.

If you are allowed to add units to your army they must conform to any Unit Selection restrictions for the battleplan being used.

Storm of Gheists/All That Glitters: No changes.

Across The Plains: The player that won Storm of Gheists receives 1 extra command point at the start of the first battle round of this battle.

The Reality Sores: The player that won Across The Plains receives 1 extra command point at the start of the first battle round of this battle.

A Fate Postponed: The winner of All That Glitters receives 1 extra command point at the start of the first battle round of this battle if they won a **minor victory**, or D3 extra command points at the start of the first battle round if they won a **major victory**.

A Clash of Gods: The Teclis player can add 1 **Lumineth Realm-lords** unit to their army for each **major victory** they have won so far in the campaign. The Nagash player can add 1 **Ossiarch Bonereapers** unit to their army for each **major victory** they have won so far in the campaign.

CAMPAIGN VICTORY

If one player is victorious in Storm of Gheists, A Fate Postponed and A Clash of Gods, they win a **total campaign victory**. If one player is victorious in A Clash of Gods and either Storm of Gheists or A Fate Postponed, they win a **strategic campaign victory**. In any other circumstances, the victor in A Clash of Gods wins a **tactical campaign victory**.

ALTERNATIVE ARMIES

If you don't have all of the units or armies needed to fight a campaign, just substitute suitable units that you do have for the ones that you don't. For example, if the player using the Null Myriad army in A Fate Postponed didn't have any Gothizzar Harvesters, they could substitute them for **Ossiarch Bonereapers** units they do have.

STREETS OF DEATH

The Mortal Realms are studded with settlements, ranging from mighty walled strongholds through to dung-filled wooden shanty towns. At times of war it is extremely common for ferocious battles to be fought amidst the streets, buildings and alleyways of these hubs of civilisation.

Sometimes a battleplan will use only some of the Streets of Death rules. In this case, it will list the rules that apply. If a battleplan simply says to use the Streets of Death rules, then all of the following rules apply.

The Streets of Death rules are divided into two types: those that can be used with any battleplan, and those that can only be used with battleplans that have an attacker and a defender. If a battleplan has an attacker and defender, it will describe how to decide who is the attacker and who is the defender.

The Streets of Death rules often refer to 'buildings'. For rules purposes, a building is any terrain feature that can be garrisoned. In addition, the players can agree that any other terrain features they wish should count as buildings (Azyrite Ruins, for example).

Barricades: *The defenders of a besieged settlement will often place barricades across the streets.*

After set-up is complete but before the battle begins, the defender can set up any number of barricades in their territory. Each barricade must stretch from one building to a different building that is within 8" of the first. The barricade can be represented by Walls and Fences, or any other suitable models in the player's collection. Barricades are obstacles.

If a unit is within 1" of a barricade at the start of its movement phase and there are no enemy units within 6" of that barricade, that unit can knock that barricade down instead of making a normal move; if they do so, remove the barricade from the battlefield. A barricade that has been knocked down cannot be set up again.

Bricks and Stones: *The terrified citizens of a settlement can hurl bricks, roof slates and other improvised missiles at their tormentors.*

At the start of their shooting phase, the defender can make 1 Bricks and Stones attack from each building in their territory that has not been cleared (see below). To make a Bricks and Stones attack, pick 1 enemy unit within 6" of that building and roll a dice. On a 5+, that enemy unit suffers D3 mortal wounds.

A building is cleared when an enemy unit garrisons the building. The defender cannot make Bricks and Stones attacks from a building once it has been cleared, even if the enemy unit garrisoning that building stops garrisoning it, or if any of the defender's units garrison it.

Hidden Defenders: *Fighting through the streets of a settlement is a tense and dangerous affair, where every building could house hidden defenders.*

Instead of setting them up on the battlefield, the defender can place any of their units to one side and say that they are set up in hiding as reserve units. They must declare that they are doing so for each such unit, and then secretly pick an unoccupied building wholly within their territory and make a note that the unit is hiding in that building. Hidden units are treated as garrisoning that building and must conform to any limitations that apply to garrisoning units.

The defender can reveal the location of any hidden units in their hero phase. In addition, they must reveal a hidden unit if an enemy unit attempts to garrison the building it is hiding in, the building it is hiding in collapses, or the building it is hiding in is set on fire. If a hidden unit is revealed because an enemy unit attempts to garrison the building it is hiding in, the enemy unit cannot garrison the building and cannot move in the movement phase in which it attempted to do so.

Narrow Streets: *The narrow streets of a settlement are dangerous ground for mounted units, who risk crashing into the walls on either side of the street if they advance along them at anything other than a walking pace.*

A narrow street is any area of open ground between two buildings that are 4" or less apart. If a **Monster** or a model with a mount makes a run move or charge move, and any part of that move was on a narrow street, roll a dice after the move has been made. On a 1, that model's unit suffers 1 mortal wound after all of the models in the unit have been moved. Only roll for models that can fly if they finish a run move or a charge move on a narrow street.

REALMS OF BATTLE

On the following pages you will find three new sets of Realms of Battle rules that allow you to fight battles set in the regions of the Mortal Realms described in the narrative section of this book. These rules are suitable for narrative and open play games but are not intended for matched play.

REALM OF BATTLE: PRAETORIS, SHYISH

REALMSPHERE MAGIC
Drain Vitality: *This cursed spell saps a foe's strength, leaving them weak and vulnerable.*

Drain Vitality has a casting value of 6. If successfully cast, pick 1 enemy unit within 18" of the caster that is visible to them. Until your next hero phase, re-roll unmodified hit rolls of 6 for attacks made by that unit, and re-roll unmodified save rolls of 6 for attacks that target that unit.

REALMSCAPE FEATURE
The Triptych: *This trio of statue-topped fortresses on the Great Plains of Praetoris is a nexus of death magic.*

DEATH WIZARDS treat all terrain features as having the Arcane scenery rule in addition to any other scenery rules that they have.

REALM ARTEFACT
Sepulchral Plate: *The deathly energies of this black plate seep into the wearer's wounds, substituting injury with unnatural vitality.*

Roll a dice each time you allocate a wound to the bearer. On a 6, that wound is negated.

REALM COMMAND
Full Tilt!: *The flat plains of Praetoris allow mounted units to advance at a blistering pace.*

You can use this command ability at the start of your movement phase. If you do so, pick 1 friendly unit that has mounts and is wholly within 12" of a friendly **HERO**. That unit can run in that movement phase and still charge later in the same turn.

REALM OF BATTLE: INVIDIA, GHYRAN

REALMSPHERE MAGIC
Cloying Quagmire: *The sorcerer thrusts their hands into the soil, causing the ground to liquefy into a sucking, gasping quagmire.*

Cloying Quagmire has a casting value of 5. If successfully cast, pick 1 enemy unit within 14" of the caster that is visible to them and roll a dice. If the roll is equal to or greater than that unit's Save characteristic, that unit suffers D6 mortal wounds.

REALMSCAPE FEATURE
Thumb-sized Mosquitos: *The ruin-dotted swamps of Invida are home to blood-sucking insects that are of a monstrous size.*

At the start of the enemy movement phase, you can pick up to D3 enemy units. Roll a dice for each unit. On a 1-3 nothing happens. On a 4-5, that unit suffers 1 mortal wound. On a 6, that unit suffers 1 mortal wound and cannot run in that phase.

REALM COMMAND
Submerge: *The swamplands of Invidia can provide protection from enemy attacks to those warriors who are willing to submerge themselves in its foetid waters.*

You can use this command ability at the start of the enemy shooting phase. If you do so, pick 1 friendly unit that is wholly within 12" of a friendly **HERO**. Apply the cover modifier to save rolls for that unit until the end of that phase.

REALM ARTEFACT
The Fecund Flask: *The bearer of this flask can drink deep of its endless contents, allowing the poisonous blessings of Nurgle to restore their vitality – though not always in the way the imbiber may have hoped.*

Once per battle, at the start of your hero phase, you can roll a dice for the bearer. On a 2+, all wounds allocated the bearer are healed. On a 1, the bearer is slain, but before they are removed you can add 1 **BEASTS OF NURGLE** unit with 1 model to your army. Set up the unit within 1" of the bearer, then remove the bearer.

REALM OF BATTLE: YMETRICA, HYSH

REALMSPHERE MAGIC

Folds in Perception: *The caster bends the light of Hysh in such a way that their allies are hidden in plain sight from the enemy.*

Folds in Perception has a casting value of 6. If successfully cast, pick 2 points on the battlefield within 12" of the caster and within 12" of each other. Until your next hero phase, friendly models are not visible to enemy models that cannot fly if an imaginary straight line 1mm wide drawn between the closest points of the two models passes between those 2 points.

REALMSCAPE FEATURE

Mountainous Landscape: *The Hyshian paradise of Ymetrica is dominated by soaring mountains. Marching armies can only find passage between the peaks by using the valleys that lie between them.*

Reserve units that must be set up within a certain distance of the edge of the battlefield can only be set up within that distance of the two narrow edges of the battlefield.

REALM COMMAND

Hidden Pathways: *A wise commander will send scouts to discover hidden pathways across the mountain ranges that dominate these lands.*

You can use this command ability when you set up a reserve unit that must be set up within a certain distance of the edge of the battlefield. If you do so, you can ignore the Mountainous Landscape realmscape feature when you set up that unit.

REALM ARTEFACT

Prism of Amyntok: *This prism can focus the light of Hysh into a devastating beam.*

In your shooting phase, you can pick 1 enemy unit within 8" of the bearer that is visible to them and roll 4 dice. For each 6, that unit suffers 1 mortal wound.

STORM OF GHEISTS

The city of Settler's Gain in Hysh was a place of high spires and soaring achievement, built from nothing at the dawn of the Age of Sigmar. Yet even the favour of its Lumineth sponsors did not mean it was immune to the crippling effects of the Necroquake. In the space of a single night, Hysh's foremost human city had transformed from a bulwark of glittering sanctity to a place of the blackest terror.

STREETS OF DEATH
Use the Streets of Death rules (pg 72).

THE ARMIES
One player is the Settler's Gain player. Their opponent is the Nighthaunt player.

Settler's Gain Army
The Settler's Gain player is the defender and must use a Settler's Gain Cities of Sigmar army (pg 96). It must consist of the following units and warscroll battalion:

- 9 **Settler's Gain** units
- Xintil War-magi (pg 97)

Nighthaunt Army
The Nighthaunt player is the attacker and must use a Nighthaunt army. It must consist of the following units:

- 16 **Nighthaunt** units

Unit Selection
The units in each army must conform to one of the types in the following list. You can double the size of a unit if you wish, but it then counts as 2 choices instead of 1.

Regular Unit: A unit of up to 10 models, each with a Wounds characteristic of 1.

Elite Unit: A unit of up to 5 models, each with a Wounds characteristic of 2 or 3.

Guard Unit: A unit of up to 3 models, each with a Wounds characteristic of 4 or 5.

Linebreaker Unit: A unit of 1 model with a Wounds characteristic of more than 5 that is not a **Hero** or **Monster**.

Champion: A **Hero** with a Wounds characteristic of 8 or less.

REALMS OF BATTLE
This battle uses the rules for Ymetrica, Hysh (pg 75).

OBJECTIVES
Set up objectives as shown on the map.

SET-UP
The Settler's Gain player sets up their army first, wholly within their territory. All units from the Xintil War-magi battalion must be set up in reserve as reinforcements (they cannot be hidden units).

The Nighthaunt player sets up their army second, wholly within their territory and more than 3" from any enemy units.

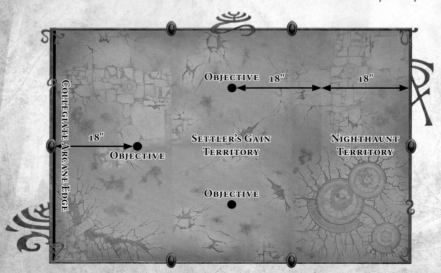

FIRST TURN

The Nighthaunt player takes the first turn in the first battle round.

THE WAR-MAGI

At the end of any of the Settler's Gain player's movement phases, they can set up the units from the Xintil War-magi warscroll battalion wholly within 6" of the Collegiate Arcane edge of the battlefield and more than 9" from any enemy units.

BATTLE LENGTH

Starting from the third battle round, at the end of each battle round, roll a dice and add the number of the current battle round to the roll. On a 9+, the battle ends. On any other roll, the battle continues.

GLORIOUS VICTORY

The Settler's Gain player wins a **major victory** at the end of the battle if they control at least 2 objectives and the Xintil War-magi battalion was not set up before the fourth battle round.

The Settler's Gain player wins a **minor victory** at the end of the battle if they control at least 2 objectives and the Xintil War-magi battalion was set up before the fourth battle round.

The Nighthaunt player wins a **minor victory** at the end of the battle if they control 2 objectives.

The Nighthaunt player wins a **major victory** at the end of the battle if they control 3 objectives.

BATTLEPLAN
ACROSS THE PLAINS

Echelons of Lumineth Realm-lords cavalry were able to penetrate deeply into Equuis Main, the territory of the Stalliarch Lords. That shining company, gleaming in the darkness, was an open challenge that the Liege-Kavaloi of Equuis could not ignore.

THE ARMIES
One player is the Lumineth Realm-lords player. Their opponent is the Stalliarch Lords player.

Lumineth Realm-lords Army
The Lumineth Realm-lords player must use a Lumineth Realm-lords army. It must consist of the following units:

- 12 **Lumineth Realm-lords** units

Stalliarch Lords Army
The Stalliarch Lords player must use a Stalliarch Lords Ossiarch Bonereapers army. It must consist of the following units and warscroll battalion:

- 9 **Stalliarch Lords** units
- Horrek's Dreadlance (pg 101)

Unit Selection
The units in each army must conform to one of the types in the following list. You can double the size of a unit if you wish, but it then counts as 2 choices instead of 1.

Elite Mounted Unit: A unit of up to 5 models, each with a Wounds characteristic of 2 or 3 and a mount.

Mounted Champion: A **Hero** with a Wounds characteristic of 8 or less that has a mount or can fly.

REALMS OF BATTLE
This battle uses the rules for Praetoris, Shyish (pg 73).

SET-UP
The players alternate setting up units one at a time, starting with the Lumineth Realm-lords player. Players must set up their units wholly within their territory and more than 12" from enemy territory. Continue to set up units until both players have set up their armies. If one player finishes first, their opponent must set up the rest of the units in their army, one after another.

FIRST TURN
The Lumineth Realm-lords player takes the first turn in the first battle round.

MOVING OBJECTIVES
If you control an objective at the start of your movement phase, you can say that 1 friendly model within 1" of that objective will move it. If you do so, place the objective marker so that it is touching the base of that model. In that movement phase, if you move that model, move the objective marker so that it is once again touching the base of that model.

ESCAPE

If a **Lumineth Realm-lords** model with an objective is within 6" of the exit point (see map) at the start of the Lumineth Realm-lords player's turn, that model must escape: remove it and the objective from play.

BATTLE LENGTH

Starting from the third battle round, at the end of each battle round, roll a dice and add the number of the current battle round to the roll. On a 9+, the battle ends. On any other roll, the battle continues.

GLORIOUS VICTORY

The Lumineth Realm-lords player wins a **major victory** if at least 2 friendly models escaped with objectives.

The Lumineth Realm-lords player wins a **minor victory** if 1 friendly model escaped with an objective.

The Stalliarch Lords player wins a **minor victory** if no enemy models escaped with objectives and they control at least 1 objective.

The Stalliarch Lords player wins a **major victory** if no enemy models escaped with objectives and they control at least 2 objectives.

Any other result is a **draw**.

THE REALITY SORES

Riding into hagfish-choked waters, a host of mounted wights struck deep into Invidia. Horticulous Slimux gathered his fellow Heralds and moved to block the cavalry force encroaching on his domain. With him went the Spoilpox Scrivener known as Noddrack the Snitch and the capering Sloppity Bilepiper Gortle Pulpskull. Together the three Heralds formed a tripartite defence, a bulwark of daemon flesh that could draw on near limitless reinforcements from the Reality Sores.

THE ARMIES

One player is the Maggotkin player. Their opponent is the Legion of Night player.

Maggotkin Army

The Maggotkin player must use a Nurgle army. It must consist of the following units and warscroll battalion:

- Horticulous Slimux
- 9 **Nurgle Daemon** units
- Invidian Plaguehost (pg 95)

Legion of Night Army

The Legion of Night player must use a **Legion of Night** Legions of Nagash army. It must consist of the following units:

- 18 **Legion of Night** units

Unit Selection

The units in each army must conform to one of the types in the following list. You can double the size of a unit if you wish, but it then counts as 2 choices instead of 1.

Regular Unit: A unit of up to 10 models, each with a Wounds characteristic of 1.

Elite Unit: A unit of up to 5 models, each with a Wounds characteristic of 2 or 3.

Guard Unit: A unit of up to 3 models, each with a Wounds characteristic of 4 or 5.

Linebreaker Unit: A unit of 1 model with a Wounds characteristic of more than 5 that is not a **Hero** or **Monster**.

Champion: A **Hero** with a Wounds characteristic of 8 or less.

REALMS OF BATTLE

This battle uses the rules for Invidia, Ghyran (pg 74).

SET-UP

The Maggotkin player sets up their army first, wholly within their territory and more than 12" from enemy territory.

The Legion of Night player sets up their army second, wholly within their territory and more than 6" from enemy territory.

FIRST TURN

The Legion of Night player takes the first turn in the first battle round.

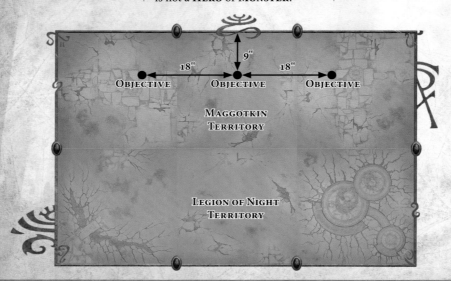

PRESS THEM HARD

At the end of each of their turns, the Legion of Night player scores 1 victory point for each objective that is within 6" of any friendly models.

At the end of each of their turns, the Maggotkin player scores 1 victory point for each objective that is not within 6" of any enemy models.

BATTLE LENGTH

The battle lasts for 5 battle rounds.

GLORIOUS VICTORY

The player with the most victory points at the end of the battle wins a **major victory**. If both players have the same number of victory points, use the tiebreaker to determine which player wins a minor victory or if the battle is a draw.

Tiebreaker

Each player adds up the number of enemy units that were destroyed during the battle, excluding any units that were added to the armies after the battle started. Double-sized units count as 2 units instead of 1.

If one player has the higher total, they win a **minor victory**. If neither player has the higher total, the battle is a **draw**.

BATTLEPLAN
ALL THAT GLITTERS

Imoda Barrasdottr, an up-and-coming Kharadron captain, discovered that Neferata had secured the realmgate known as the Switchsoul Dais and had started a ritual that could only bode ill for Chamon. Regaining her flagship, she began make haste for Barak-Zilfin. However, Neferata was not going to simply let the impudent Kharadron escape and reveal her plans to those who would seek to thwart them.

THE ARMIES
One player is the Kharadron Overlords player. Their opponent is the Legion of Blood player.

Kharadron Overlords Army
The Kharadron Overlords player must use a Barak-Zilfin Kharadron Overlords army. It must consist of the following units:

- 1 Arkanaut Admiral (Imoda Barrasdottr)
- 1 Aetheric Navigator
- 1 Endrinmaster with Endrinharness

- 1 Arkanaut Ironclad
- 2 Arkanaut Frigates
- 2 Arkanaut Companies of up to 10 models
- 1 Grundstok Thunderers unit of up to 5 models

Legion of Blood Army
The Legion of Blood player must use a **LEGION OF BLOOD** Legions of Nagash army. It must consist of the following units:

- 6 Terrorgheists or Zombie Dragons in any combination

SET-UP
The Kharadron Overlords player sets up their army first, wholly within their territory.

The Legion of Blood player sets up their army second. Each unit must be set up wholly within a different Legion of Blood territory (e.g. one unit in territory 1, one unit in territory 2, etc.).

The first Legion of Blood unit to be set up can be set up anywhere wholly within their territory. All

the remaining Legion of Blood units must be set up wholly within their territory and within 1" of the edge of the battlefield.

HARKRAKEN LAIRS
After armies are set up, but before the first battle round begins, roll a D6. The Legion of Blood territory with the same number as the roll is the location of the Harkraken Lairs.

At the start of the first battle round, before determining who has the first turn, roll a dice for each **SKYVESSEL** and **MONSTER** that is at least partially in the location of the Harkraken Lairs. On a 1-3, nothing happens. On a 4-5, that unit suffers D3 mortal wounds. On a 6, that unit suffers D6 mortal wounds.

LONG WAY UP
Kharadron Overlords units that are unable to fly can only be set up as garrisons of **SKYVESSELS** wholly within their territory. These units cannot leave the

SKYVESSEL they are garrisoning; if forced to do so for any reason, they are slain. In addition, **SKYVESSELS** cannot use their Fly High ability in this battle.

LONG WAY DOWN

At the start of the battleshock phase, roll a dice for each successful save roll made in that turn for an attack that targeted a Kharadron Overlords garrison unit. On a 1, 1 model in that unit is slain. Models slain in this manner count towards the unit's battleshock test.

ESCAPE TO BARAK-ZILFIN

If a **SKYVESSEL** is within 6" of the exit point at the start of the Kharadron Overlords player's turn, that model must escape: remove it from play.

BATTLE LENGTH

The battle lasts until there are no Kharadron Overlords models left on the battlefield.

GLORIOUS VICTORY

The Kharadron Overlords player wins a **major victory** at the end of the battle if 3 **SKYVESSELS** escaped. The Kharadron Overlords player wins a **minor victory** at the end of the battle if 2 **SKYVESSELS** escaped.

The Legion of Blood player wins a **minor victory** at the end of the battle if only 1 **SKYVESSEL** escaped. The Legion of Blood player wins a **major victory** at the end of the battle if no **SKYVESSELS** escaped.

A FATE POSTPONED

At first, the assault upon Ymetrica by the Null Myriad under Arkhan proved unstoppable. The Lumineth learned quickly, however, and through great sacrifice were able to slow and then halt the Myriad's advance. Then Sevireth, Lord of the Seventh Wind, came searing through the mountain vales at the head of a leaping, shouting spearhead of Hurakan warriors, and the Realm-lords' methodical campaign to cut off their foe's supply of bone turned into a joyous, headlong assault.

THE ARMIES
One player is the Null Myriad player. Their opponent is the Lumineth Realm-lords player.

Lumineth Realm-lords Army
The Lumineth Realm-lords player must use an Ymetrica Lumineth Realm-lords army. It must consist of the following units:

- Sevireth, Lord of the Seventh Wind
- 16 **Ymetrica** units

Null Myriad Army
The Null Myriad player must use a Null Myriad Ossiarch Bonereapers army. It must consist of the following units:

- Arkhan the Black
- 2 Gothizzar Harvesters
- 12 **Null Myriad** units

Unit Selection
The units in each army must conform to one of the types in the following list. You can double the size of a unit if you wish, but it then counts as 2 choices instead of 1.

Regular Unit: A unit of up to 10 models, each with a Wounds characteristic of 1.

Elite Unit: A unit of up to 5 models, each with a Wounds characteristic of 2 or 3.

Guard Unit: A unit of up to 3 models, each with a Wounds characteristic of 4 or 5.

Linebreaker Unit: A unit of 1 model with a Wounds characteristic of more than 5 that is not a **Hero** or **Monster**.

Champion: A **Hero** with a Wounds characteristic of 8 or less.

REALMS OF BATTLE
This battle uses the rules for Ymetrica, Hysh (pg 75).

SET-UP
The Lumineth Realm-lords player sets up their army first. All **Hurakan** units are set up in reserve. All other units must be set up wholly within Lumineth Realm-lords territory more than 9" from enemy territory. The Null Myriad player sets up their army second, wholly within their territory and more than 9" from enemy territory.

NULL MYRIAD TERRITORY   LUMINETH REALM-LORDS TERRITORY

FIRST TURN
The Null Myriad player takes the first turn in the first battle round.

SACRIFICE OF ASHES
The Null Myriad player cannot heal wounds allocated to a friendly unit while it is within 30" of a **Starshard Ballistas** unit, within 18" of an enemy **Wizard**, or within 6" of Sevireth, Lord of the Seventh Wind.

SEVIRETH'S ARRIVAL
At the end of the Lumineth Realm-lords player's third movement phase, they must set up their **Hurakan** units wholly within 12" of the edge the battlefield and more than 6" from any enemy units; the Mountainous Landscape realmscape feature is ignored.

BATTLE LENGTH
The battle lasts for 5 battle rounds.

GLORIOUS VICTORY
At the end of the battle, each player adds up the number of enemy units that were destroyed during the battle, excluding any units that were added to the armies after the battle started. Double-sized units count as 2 units instead of 1.

If one player's total that is at least double their opponent's total, they win a **major victory**. If one player's total is higher but less than double their opponent's total, they win a **minor victory**. If neither player has the higher total, the battle is a **draw**.

BATTLEPLAN
A CLASH OF GODS

Teclis and Nagash are locked in an epic duel fought on both the physical and spiritual planes. As each tries to wrest the advantage, immense armies are engaged in an equally titanic battle all around them. From moment to moment, one side and then the other is in the ascendant, desperately seeking the key to victory; the fate of Ymetrica will be decided by whichever is able to do so first.

THE ARMIES
One player is the Teclis player. Their opponent is the Nagash player.

Teclis' Army
The Teclis player must use an Ymetrica Lumineth Realm-lords army that has Teclis as its general. It must consist of the following units and warscroll battalion:

- Archmage Teclis and Celennar, Spirit of Hysh
- 20 **Ymetrica** units
- 1 allied Xintil War-magi (pg 97)
- 2 allied **Collegiate Arcane** units

Nagash's Army
The Nagash player must use a Mortis Praetorians Ossiarch Bonereapers army that has Nagash as its general. It must consist of the following units and warscroll battalion:

- Nagash, Supreme Lord of the Undead
- 20 **Mortis Praetorians** units
- 1 allied Mortevell's Helcourt (pg 100)
- 2 allied **Crypt Ghouls** units

REALMS OF BATTLE
This battle uses the rules for Ymetrica, Hysh (pg 75).

SET-UP
First, set up Teclis and Nagash so they are within 3" of each other and the centre of the battlefield. No other units can be set up within 3" of Teclis or Nagash.

Then the Nagash player sets up their army. All **Flesh-eater Courts** units are set up in reserve. All **Ossiarch**

Bonereapers units must be set up wholly within Ossiarch Bonereapers territory and more than 9" from enemy territory.

Then the Teclis player sets up their army. All **Collegiate Arcane** units are set up in reserve. All **Vanari** and **Scinari** units must be set up wholly within Vanari/Scinari territory, all **Alarith** units must be set up wholly within Alarith territory, and all **Hurakan** units must be set up wholly within Hurakan territory.

REINFORCEMENTS
At the end of any of the Nagash player's movement phases, they can set up any of their **Flesh-eater Courts** units wholly within 6" of the battlefield edge in Alarith territory and more than 3" from any enemy units.

Starting from the third battle round, at the end of any of the Teclis player's movement phases, they can set up any of their **Collegiate Arcane** units wholly within 6" of the edge the

VANARI/SCINARI TERRITORY

ALARITH TERRITORY

OSSIARCH BONEREAPERS TERRITORY

OBJECTIVE

HURAKAN TERRITORY

XINTIL WAR-MAGI TERRITORY

battlefield in Xintil War-magi territory and more than 3" from any enemy units.

STRUGGLE OF TITANS

No units can move within 3" of Teclis or Nagash during this battle (even when making a charge or pile-in move). Teclis and Nagash cannot move, attack, cast spells or use abilities or command abilities, and they cannot be picked to be the target of attacks, spells, abilities or command abilities. Any wounds inflicted upon them are negated and they cannot be slain.

BATTLE LENGTH

The battle lasts until either Nagash or Teclis are cast down (see below).

GLORIOUS VICTORY

At the end of each battle round, each player rolls a dice. Each player adds 1 to their roll if more enemy units than friendly units were destroyed during that battle round.

Each player adds 1 to their roll if there are more friendly **WIZARDS** than enemy **WIZARDS** on the battlefield.

The Teclis player adds 1 to their roll if there are more friendly models than enemy models within 12" of Teclis.

The Nagash player adds 1 to their roll if there are more friendly models than enemy models within 12" of Nagash.

If one player's roll is higher, the enemy general is *weakened*. If the general is already weakened, they are *stunned*. If the general has already been stunned, they are *cast down*. The player that casts down the enemy general wins a **major victory**.

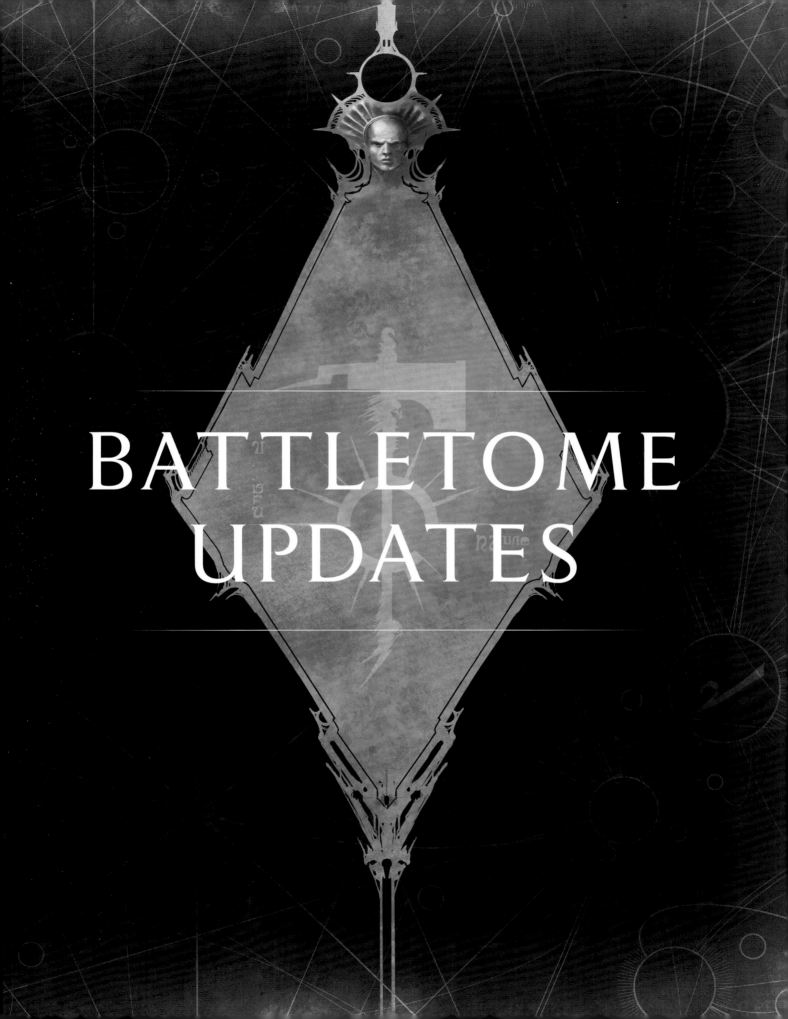

BATTLETOME UPDATES

BATTLETOME UPDATES

This section of *Broken Realms: Teclis* includes updates to four battletomes which allow you to use the armies described in the narrative section of the book in your games of Warhammer Age of Sigmar. The updates are designed to be used with the battleplans in this book, and can also be used in matched play.

MAGGOTKIN OF NURGLE (pg 92-95)
This update to *Battletome: Maggotkin of Nurgle* contains the Invidian Plaguehost warscroll battalion and updated warscrolls for the Sloppity Bilepiper, Spoilpox Scrivener and Beasts of Nurgle.

CITIES OF SIGMAR (pg 96-99)
This update to *Battletome: Cities of Sigmar* contains the Xintil War-magi warscroll battalion and Settler's Gain allegiance abilities.

FLESH-EATER COURTS (pg 100)
This update to *Battletome: Flesh-eater Courts* contains the Mortevell's Helcourt warscroll battalion, allowing you to represent Gorstane Mortevell and his sycophantic courtiers in your games.

OSSIARCH BONEREAPERS (pg 101)
This update to *Battletome: Ossiarch Bonereapers* contains the Horrek's Dreadlance warscroll battalion, allowing you to represent Liege-Kavalos Horrek Venzai and his infamous Dreadlance in your games.

SLOPPITY BILEPIPER
HERALD OF NURGLE

MOVE	4"	
WOUNDS	5	
SAVE	5+	
BRAVERY	10	

Sloppity Bilepipers caper through the ranks of Nurgle's legions as they advance. Infected with a plague of mirth, they prance and quip, entertaining their fellow daemons even as they cause the enemy to literally die laughing.

MELEE WEAPONS	Range	Attacks	To Hit	To Wound	Rend	Damage
Marotter	1"	4	4+	3+	-1	2

DESCRIPTION

A Sloppity Bilepiper is a single model armed with a Marotter.

ABILITIES

Disgustingly Resilient: *Daemons of Nurgle are inured to pain, their rotting bodies shrugging off all but the most traumatic damage with ease.*

Roll a dice each time you allocate a wound or mortal wound to this model. On a 5+, that wound or mortal is negated.

Disease of Mirth: *Plaguebearers become even more stubbornly morose when forced to listen to a Bilepiper's jokes, while Nurgle's other daemons find them hilarious.*

Add 1 to the Bravery characteristic of friendly **NURGLE DAEMON** units while they are wholly within 14" of any friendly **SLOPPITY BILEPIPERS**.

Jolly Gutpipes: *Bilepipers have a suitably revolting repertoire to draw upon in battle.*

At the start of the combat phase, you can say that this model will play a revolting tune. If you do so, pick 1 of the following tunes. The effect of that tune lasts until the end of that phase. A unit cannot benefit from a tune more than once per phase. If a unit is affected by 2 or more different tunes, none of those tunes have an effect on that unit in that phase.

A Stabbing We Will Go!: Add 1 to the Attacks characteristic of melee weapons used by friendly **NURGLE DAEMON** units that are wholly within 14" of any friendly **SLOPPITY BILEPIPERS** playing this tune.

Early One Evening My Pustule Was Seeping: If the unmodified hit roll for an attack made by a friendly **NURGLE DAEMON** unit wholly within 14" of any friendly **SLOPPITY BILEPIPERS** playing this tune is 6, that attack inflicts 1 mortal wound on the target in addition to any normal damage.

My Love Is Like a Ripe, Ripe Fart: Enemy models within 3" of a friendly **NURGLE DAEMON** unit that is wholly within 14" of any friendly **SLOPPITY BILEPIPERS** playing this tune cannot finish pile-in moves closer to a model from that unit than they were at the start of the move.

KEYWORDS	CHAOS, DAEMON, PLAGUEBEARER, NURGLE, HERO, SLOPPITY BILEPIPER, HERALD OF NURGLE

SPOILPOX SCRIVENER
HERALD OF NURGLE

MOVE	4"					
WOUNDS	5	SAVE	5+			
BRAVERY	10					

Spoilpox Scriveners keep a strict watch over the tallying efforts of the Plaguebearers. Should the enemy stray too close, the Heralds bite off heads and limbs with their huge distended maws, or blanket the enemy in diseased mucus with almighty sneezes.

MISSILE WEAPONS	Range	Attacks	To Hit	To Wound	Rend	Damage
Disgusting Sneezes	6"	D6	2+	4+	-	1
MELEE WEAPONS	Range	Attacks	To Hit	To Wound	Rend	Damage
Distended Maw	2"	2	3+	3+	-1	2

DESCRIPTION

A Spoilpox Scrivener is a single model armed with a Distended Maw and Disgusting Sneezes.

ABILITIES

Disgustingly Resilient: *Daemons of Nurgle are inured to pain, their rotting bodies shrugging off all but the most traumatic damage with ease.*

Roll a dice each time you allocate a wound or mortal wound to this model. On a 5+, that wound or mortal is negated.

Keep Counting, I'm Watching You: *Spoilpox Scriveners are responsible for making sure that the Plaguebearers of their Tallyband do not shirk.*

At the start of the combat phase, you can say that this model will call for 1 count. If you do so, pick 1 friendly **PLAGUEBEARER** unit wholly within 14" of this model and pick 1 of the following counts for that unit to carry out. The effect of that count lasts until the end of that phase. A unit cannot carry out more than 1 count per phase.

Tally of Blows: Add 1 to the Attacks characteristic of melee weapons used by a unit carrying out this count.

Studied Lacerations: Improve the Rend characteristic of melee weapons used by a unit carrying out this count by 1.

Recorded Stamina: Add 1 to save rolls for attacks that target a unit carrying out this count.

KEYWORDS	CHAOS, DAEMON, PLAGUEBEARER, NURGLE, HERO, SPOILPOX SCRIVENER, HERALD OF NURGLE

MOVE **5"**

WOUNDS **8**

SAVE **5+**

BRAVERY **10**

BEASTS OF NURGLE

Beasts of Nurgle are huge, slug-like abominations that are possessed of an exuberance at odds with their horrific appearance. They gleefully rip and crush their 'playmates' until their joy proves lethal, before lolloping off in search of new victims.

MELEE WEAPONS	Range	Attacks	To Hit	To Wound	Rend	Damage
Clawed Limbs and Fanged Maw	1"	4	4+	3+	-1	2
Tentacles and Slobbering Tongue	1"	D6	4+	3+	-	1

DESCRIPTION

A unit of Beasts of Nurgle has any number of models, each armed with Clawed Limbs and a Fanged Maw, and Tentacles and a Slobbering Tongue.

ABILITIES

Disgustingly Resilient: *Daemons of Nurgle are inured to pain, their rotting bodies shrugging off all but the most traumatic damage with ease.*

Roll a dice each time you allocate a wound or mortal wound to this model. On a 5+, that wound or mortal is negated.

Acid Slime Trails: *Paralytic goo seeps from the skin of these disgusting creatures.*

Before this unit makes a retreat move, roll a dice for each enemy unit within 3" of this unit. On a 4+, that unit suffers D3 mortal wounds.

Attention Seekers: *Beasts of Nurgle seek out playmates with an enthusiasm that is rarely reciprocated by the horrified objects of their desire.*

This unit can run and/or retreat and still charge later in the same turn. In addition, when this unit retreats, it can pass across other models in the same manner as a model that can fly.

Pestilent Battering Rams: *Beasts of Nurgle smash into enemy battlelines, crushing the enemy and unleashing myriad plagues as they flail around with joy.*

After a model from this unit finishes a charge move, roll a dice for each enemy unit within 1" of that model. On a 2+, that unit suffers D3 mortal wounds. If this unit has more than 1 model, roll to determine if mortal wounds are inflicted after each model finishes its charge move, but do not allocate the mortal wounds until all of the models in the unit have finished their charge moves.

KEYWORDS	CHAOS, DAEMON, NURGLE, BEASTS OF NURGLE

WARSCROLL BATTALION
INVIDIAN PLAGUEHOST

Slumping, shuffling, and slouching comes the Plaguehost of Invidia, massed ranks of Plaguebearers tallying the new diseases they visit upon the foe. Lucky, then, they have Noddrack the Snitch to drive them on and Gortle Pulpskull to raise their spirits – or at the very least, incentivise them to finish the job quickly…

ORGANISATION

- 1 Sloppity Bilepiper (Gortle Pulpskull)

- 1 Spoilpox Scrivener (Noddrack the Snitch)

- 2 Plaguebearers units

The Sloppity Bilepiper and Spoilpox Scrivener from this battalion are unique named characters.

ABILITIES

Bulwark of Flesh: *The Invidian Plaguehost can draw on numerous reinforcements from the Reality Sores.*

The first time a Plaguebearers unit from this battalion is destroyed, a new Plaguebearers unit with 10 models is added to your army. Set up the unit wholly within your territory, wholly within 6" of the edge of the battlefield, and more than 9" from any enemy units.

COMMAND TRAIT

If Gortle Pulpskull is your army's general, he must have this command trait instead of one from *Battletome: Maggotkin of Nurgle*:

Rude Limericks: *Pulpskull's limericks elicit great groans from his fellow Plaguebearers and send their glum resolve plunging to new depths.*

Add 1 to the Bravery characteristic of **NURGLE DAEMON** units from this battalion while they are wholly within 14" of the **SLOPPITY BILEPIPER** from the same battalion (in addition to the modifier from the Disease of Mirth ability).

CITIES OF SIGMAR
FREE CITIES BATTLE TRAITS

SETTLER'S GAIN

CITY OF LEARNING
Settler's Gain was a place of safety and learning for generations, but even it was not immune to the effects of the Necroquake.

When you choose a keyword for a Cities of Sigmar army using the Strongholds of Order battle trait in *Battletome: Cities of Sigmar*, you can choose the **SETTLER'S GAIN** keyword instead of one of those listed. The allegiance abilities for Settler's Gain armies can be found on pages 100-101.

WARSCROLL BATTALION
XINTIL WAR-MAGI

An air of eccentric jubilation fills the air as Xintil's finest battle wizards bring their creations to the front line. The visionary Hyshian mage Arcobalde Lazerne leads the way, using his Luminark, *Beacon of Intellect*, to protect his comrades and send beams of intense Hyshian energy burning into the ranks of his adversaries.

ORGANISATION

- 1 Battlemage (Arcobalde Lazerne)

- 1 Luminark of Hysh (*Beacon of Intellect*)

- 1 Celestial Hurricanum with Celestial Battlemage

The Battlemage from this battalion is a unique named character and must be from Hysh. All units from this battalion must have the **SETTLER'S GAIN** keyword.

ABILITIES
Beacon of Intellect: *The lens array of this mighty Luminark has been modified by none other than Arcobalde Lazerne, master of the Collegiate Arcane mages in Settler's Gain.*

When you use the Searing Beam of Light ability for the Luminark of Hysh from this battalion, you can re-roll the roll that determines if a unit suffers D3 mortal wounds. In addition, when you use the Aura of Protection ability for the Luminark of Hysh from this battalion, add 1 to the roll that determines if a wound or mortal wound is negated.

SETTLER'S GAIN BATTLE TRAITS

CITY OF LUMINARIES
SETTLER'S GAIN armies only.

IN THE LAND OF ENLIGHTENMENT
This city of gleaming spires is located in Xintil, the central paradise of Hysh.

A Settler's Gain army must be from Hysh.

LUMINETH TUTORS
Under the Lumineth's tutelage, the human wizards and artificers of Settler's Gain are able to cast spells and produce magical objects of astounding power.

You can choose 1 extra **SETTLER'S GAIN FREEGUILD HERO** or **SETTLER'S GAIN COLLEGIATE ARCANE HERO** to have an artefact of power in a Settler's Gain army. In addition, you can add 1 to casting rolls for **SETTLER'S GAIN COLLEGIATE ARCANE WIZARDS**.

WARRIORS OF THE HIGH DISTRICTS
Settler's Gain is home to both Lumineth and humans. The aelves live in utopian enclaves that tower over the districts where the humans toil, but both races fight side by side in times of war.

When you choose a Settler's Gain army, 1 in every 4 units can be a **LUMINETH REALM-LORDS** unit (this is in addition to the option for 1 in every 4 units to be a **STORMCAST ETERNALS** unit). Those units gain the **CITIES OF SIGMAR** and **SETTLER'S GAIN** keywords.

COMMAND ABILITY
Aelven Training: *The human soldiery of Settler's Gain have been carefully trained and drilled by Lumineth warriors, instilling in them a stoic discipline in the face of adversity.*

You can use this command ability at the start of the battleshock phase. If you do so, pick 1 friendly **SETTLER'S GAIN LUMINETH REALM-LORDS HERO**. Do not take battleshock tests in that phase for friendly **SETTLER'S GAIN FREEGUILD** or **SETTLER'S GAIN COLLEGIATE ARCANE** units wholly within 18" of that **HERO**.

SETTLER'S GAIN COMMAND TRAITS

SCHOLARS OF SETTLER'S GAIN
SETTLER'S GAIN generals only.

D3 Command Trait

1 Personal Levitation: *This general has learnt how harness arcane energies so they can ascend at will to the High Districts of Settler's Gain.*

This general can fly.

2 Strategic Mastermind: *This general has been schooled in the most profound aspects of warfare by esteemed Lumineth.*

If this general is part of your army and on the battlefield at the start of your hero phase, roll a dice. On a 4+, you receive 1 extra command point.

3 Raging Outburst: *Constant scrutiny and arduous testing have made this general violently short-tempered.*

Add 1 to hit and wound rolls for attacks made with melee weapons by this general, but subtract 1 from save rolls for attacks made with melee weapons that target this general.

SETTLER'S GAIN ARTEFACTS OF POWER

ARTEFACTS OF THE LUMINARIES
Settler's Gain Collegiate Arcane Heroes only.

D6   Artefact of Power

1   Heart Stone: *This quaint blood-red gemstone can save those about to die.*

The first time the bearer is slain, before removing them from play, roll a dice. On a 4+, they are not slain, 1 wound allocated to them is healed, and any wounds that remain to be allocated to them are negated.

2   Talisman of Dispellation: *This lambent charm can rob endless spells of animus.*

You do not have to reduce the number of spells the bearer can attempt to cast in your hero phase if they attempted to dispel an endless spell in the same phase.

3   Silver-plated Wand: *This highly polished wand is covered with runes of arcane power.*

The bearer can attempt to cast 1 extra spell in your hero phase.

4   Blade of Leaping Bronze: *There are few blades more finely balanced blade than this.*

Pick 1 of the bearer's melee weapons. Add 2 to the Attacks characteristic of that weapon.

5   Amulet of Haste: *This unassuming amulet can give the bearer a sudden second wind.*

Roll a dice after the bearer finishes a normal move and they ran. On a 2+, the bearer can still charge later in the same turn.

6   Stone-spirit Armour: *This armour contains fragments of rock gifted to its creator by a mountain spirit of Ymetrica – or so they say.*

Roll a dice each time you allocate a wound or mortal wound to the bearer. On a 6, that wound or mortal wound is negated. In addition, each time the bearer is affected by a spell or endless spell, you can roll a dice. On a 5+, ignore the effects of that spell on the bearer.

SETTLER'S GAIN SPELL LORES

You can choose or roll for one of the following spells for each **Collegiate Arcane Wizard** in a Settler's Gain army.

LORE OF ILLUMINATION

D3   Spell

1   Drain Magic: *The wizard becomes the blinding centre of a magic-draining vortex.*

Drain Magic has a casting value of 6. If successfully, until your next hero phase, subtract 2 from casting, dispelling and unbinding rolls for **Wizards** within 12" of the caster.

2   Shield of Light: *The caster opens their arms wide, creating a shield of glowing energy.*

Shield of Light has a casting value of 6. If successfully cast, pick 1 friendly unit wholly within 12" of the caster. Until your next hero phase, roll a dice each time you allocate a wound or mortal wound to that unit. On a 6, that wound or mortal wound is negated.

3   Illuminate: *The wizard points at a foe and makes them clearly visible.*

Illuminate has a casting value of 6. If successfully cast, pick 1 enemy unit within 12" of the caster that is visible to them. Until your next hero phase, add 1 to hit rolls for attacks made with missile weapons that target that unit.

WARSCROLL BATTALION
MORTEVELL'S HELCOURT

Amongst the deluded cannibals of the Ymetrican Flesh-eaters, there are none more devoted to Nagash than Gorstane Mortevell. With screeching, howling invective, the ghoulish emperor drives his 'court' into a frenzy of religious devotion. To their victims, it is nothing more than a rabid display of madness.

ORGANISATION

- 1 Abhorrant Archregent (Gorstane Mortevell)

- 1 Crypt Horrors unit

- 1 Crypt Ghouls unit

The Abhorrant Archregent from this battalion is a unique named character. All units from this battalion must have the **HOLLOWMOURNE** keyword.

ABILITIES

Religious Fervour: *Mortevell's followers are chosen only from the most fervent of those Flesh-eaters who worship Nagash.*

Do not take battleshock tests for units from this battalion that are wholly within 12" of the **ABHORRANT ARCHREGENT** from the same battalion.

COMMAND TRAIT

If Gorstane Mortevell is your army's general, he must have this command trait instead of one from *Battletome: Flesh-eater Courts*:

The Bright Emperor: *Gorstane Mortevell seems himself as the foremost leader of Nagash's church, and directs his flock with a feverish, self-possessed authority.*

Once per battle, this general can use the Ravenous Crusaders command ability (see *Battletome: Flesh-eater Courts*) without a command point being spent.

WARSCROLL BATTALION
HORREK'S DREADLANCE

The Kavaloi of the Ossiarch Empire are cruel beyond measure, despite their claims to a noble dynastic order as scions of Equuis Main. They have perfected the art of the Deathrider Wedge, smashing through the enemy in a great display of slaughter before wheeling back around to re-engage at terrifying speed.

ORGANISATION

- 1 Liege-Kavalos (Horrek Venzai)

- 2 Kavalos Deathriders units

The Liege-Kavalos from this battalion is a unique named character. All units from this battalion must have the **STALLIARCH LORDS** keyword.

ABILITIES
Relentless Attackers: *Horrek Venzai utilises the characteristic cavalry tactics of the Stalliarch Lords to maximum effect, smashing the enemy asunder with repeated charges whilst ensuring they have no time to reform their ranks in between.*

Each time you pick a unit from this battalion when you use the Rally Back command ability (see *Battletome: Ossiarch Bonereapers*), roll a dice. On a 4+, you receive 1 relentless discipline point.

COMMAND TRAIT
If Horrek Venzai is your army's general, he has the Twisted Challenge command trait from *Battletome: Ossiarch Bonereapers.*

ARTEFACT OF POWER
If Horrek Venzai is included in your army, he must be the first **LIEGE** to receive an artefact of power (which means he must be given the Nadir-bound Mount artefact of power from *Battletome: Ossiarch Bonereapers*).

LUMINETH
REALM-LORDS

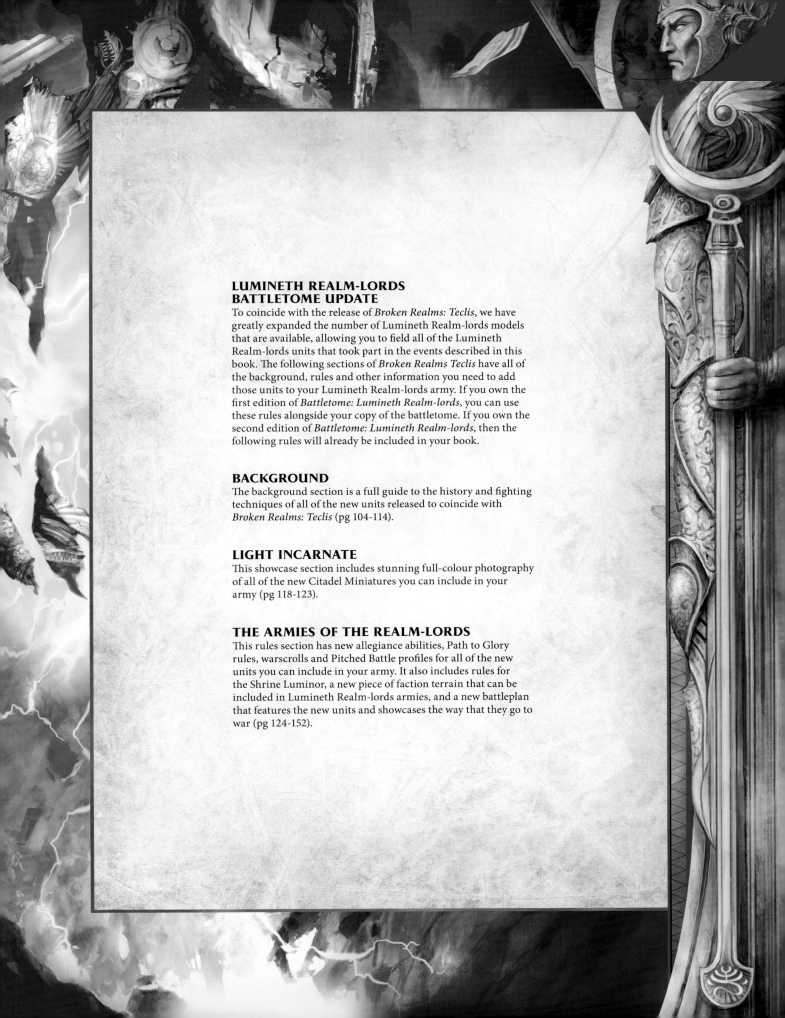

LUMINETH REALM-LORDS
BATTLETOME UPDATE

To coincide with the release of *Broken Realms: Teclis*, we have greatly expanded the number of Lumineth Realm-lords models that are available, allowing you to field all of the Lumineth Realm-lords units that took part in the events described in this book. The following sections of *Broken Realms Teclis* have all of the background, rules and other information you need to add those units to your Lumineth Realm-lords army. If you own the first edition of *Battletome: Lumineth Realm-lords*, you can use these rules alongside your copy of the battletome. If you own the second edition of *Battletome: Lumineth Realm-lords*, then the following rules will already be included in your book.

BACKGROUND

The background section is a full guide to the history and fighting techniques of all of the new units released to coincide with *Broken Realms: Teclis* (pg 104-114).

LIGHT INCARNATE

This showcase section includes stunning full-colour photography of all of the new Citadel Miniatures you can include in your army (pg 118-123).

THE ARMIES OF THE REALM-LORDS

This rules section has new allegiance abilities, Path to Glory rules, warscrolls and Pitched Battle profiles for all of the new units you can include in your army. It also includes rules for the Shrine Luminor, a new piece of faction terrain that can be included in Lumineth Realm-lords armies, and a new battleplan that features the new units and showcases the way that they go to war (pg 124-152).

ALUMNIA – THE INDOMITABLE

The aelves of Alumnia are explorers and pioneers without equal. They follow the Tyrionic tradition, always pushing forward and seeking to illuminate the realms with the light of reason and their indomitable spirit. In their quest to venture ever onwards, they have explored many of the realms' darkest corners.

As with all those Hyshian nations that revere the sun over the moon, the Alumnians are quick in mind and dexterous in body, embracing athletics over scholarship, swordcraft over magic use, action over contemplation. Yet most notable of all is their courage. The Alumnians seek to push the boundaries of mortal experience, always striving to go further than those who came before, to break new ground, to stake a claim in the direst of regions where no footstep has marred the soil until their arrival. As youths they climb precipitous mountains, swim across stormy seas, and rove across monster-haunted wildernesses just to show they can. Some of the other Great Nations claim there is a kind of arrogance in this frontiersmanship, and cast aspersions as to whether it is Alumnia's right to claim those parts of the realms that have existed for aeons without the presence of mortals. Alumnian bones litter the lairs of countless fiends and monstrosities across the Mortal Realms. Yet the surety and confidence of this Great Nation have seen it accomplish feats of civilisation no other would even attempt.

The seed of the indomitable Alumnian spirit can be found in the legend of Tyrion, god of light and first of all aelvenkind to explore the Ten Paradises. In his lonely explorations of Hysh, Tyrion strove to reach the Perimeter Inimical, passing across the Luminaris Sea to walk the fractal landscapes of Haixiah. He did so seeking not only his people from the world-that-was, but also seeking knowledge itself. Even when the landscape turned to abstraction and dissolution he strove ever on, in doing so winning the respect of the entity that was Hysh's solar limit – though it cost him his eyes, for so intense were the energies of the Perimeter Inimical they could steal the sight from even a god.

It is this great feat of exploration that the Alumnians seek to replicate. To stray across the Luminaris Sea and enter Haixiah tests even the most intrepid; many see it as a one-way journey, and none return without being irrevocably changed by the experience. Those who push across the symmetrical plains and symbol-shaped deserts of Haixiah to reach the boundary that is the Perimeter Inimical usually lose their sight in the process, blinded by the illumination of Hysh, but it is considered worth the risk for the searing insights into reality they glean as a result. Those whose extra-sensory perception or heightened auditory, olfactory and kinaesthetic senses allow them to make it back to Aluminia are known as Luminarians – though rare, they enjoy great status in the society of the Realm-lords. With energy glowing from their eye sockets and a palpable aura of power shimmering around them, they are daunting figures, the bogeymen of many a scare-tale told by human mothers to troublesome children. Some, it is rumoured, can even cause parchment or cloth to immolate with the intensity of their gaze.

When there is cause for the Lumineth to explore hazardous new regions, it is the Alumnians that are first to volunteer. They would rather die than be seen to shrink from the dangers that roam the Mortal Realms. Those abroad in the lesser realms are usually weather-beaten, worn and taciturn, striding past those who would seek their wisdom or follow them into hellish otherworlds without so much as a glance. Yet should a soul impress an Alumnian enough for them to engage in a dialogue, the supplicant may well come away from the exchange with a shard of knowledge that even a venerable seer would find astonishing.

As the Lumineth go forth into the Mortal Realms in ever greater numbers, the Alumnians find themselves in their element. Groups of Alumnian outriders and trackers go forth at the fore of hundreds of expeditions, offering their services as wayfinders, trailblazers and trackers to the Lumineth of other nations in return for the promise that they be given proper funerary rites should they venture too far in their need to push the limits of existence. Even after death the Alumnians roam, their souls crossing the underworlds of Shyish in their eternal quest to break new ground and prove themselves the masters of every domain.

HELON – CHILDREN OF THE SOLAR WINDS

The flatlands of Helon are notable not for the landscape itself, but the sentient winds that race across it and the brave Lumineth that ride the gales and cyclones. Preoccupied with matters of speed and dexterity and possessed of a highly competitive nature, the Helonites live for the thrill of outclassing those slower than themselves.

To say Helon is windswept would be a massive understatement, for it is buffeted at all times by sentient air currents. These range from capricious zephyrs that play amongst the endless golden meadows near the realm's core, all the way to the raging cyclones that tear iron-hard vegetation from the cliffs of the Luminaris Sea. The oldest of these hail from the creation of the Mortal Realms themselves, and though most of these elder winds would no sooner ally with the aelves than they would disappear into the void – for they remember well the dark times of the Ocari Dara – there are those that have made semi-permanent alliances with the Lumineth who have demonstrated enough humility to ask for their aid.

Though there are scant hills and mountains across Helon, there are an uncommon number of metaliths – the airborne islands that form the flotsam of the cosmic forces that created the realms. These are harnessed by young Lumineth across Helon for a number of purposes, foremost amongst them sport. It is common for Helonite youths to test themselves against one another by using grappling hooks and silkenrope tethers to climb high onto one of these metaliths, before employing lightweight wings or flexible patagia to fly high and fast on the racing winds that snatch them up from the vertiginous cliffs of each floating metalith. This is not merely a contest of skill or agility, but also one of spirituality and charm, for those youngsters able to convince a living wind to bear them will fly far higher and faster than any of their peers. In this way do the Helonites learn to play with the winds that race across their realm, many forming bonds that will last a lifetime.

Just like the Lumineth themselves, the winds of Helon have a competitive streak, and take great pleasure in bearing their chosen devotee faster and further than their fellow aelementors. This practice has given rise to the Great Skyrace of Helon, where young Realm-lords will swoop and dive amongst dazzling kite displays and even magical pyrotechnics as they seek to outdo each other in contests of speed, aerial dexterity and sheer will. It is scant surprise, then, that Helon boasts more Hurakan shrines than any of the other Great Nations. The floating archipelagos and lush savannahs of that realm form a paradise for wind spirits to race, frolic and spiral as they will – or at least they did before the time of the Ocari Dara, when the terrifyingly powerful spells of the Helonite Magi tore great holes in the land and cratered the unspoiled plains.

Since the Reinvention, the Lumineth of Helon have earned back a measure of trust from the aelmentors native to those lands. Many of those who once sought to ally with the winds for their own entertainment instead offered themselves as supplicants, so the spirits of the air might use them rather than the other way around. Through hard labour they put right that which had been torn down across the natural wildernesses of Helon, and in doing so, they won back the respect of the Helonite winds. The wind spirits allied to Helon's aelementiri are the most powerful of their kind, and the nation's archers are famed across the realm. Even the fierce desert wind Sevireth has deigned to fight alongside the Lumineth of Helon at times, their mutual animosity towards the scions of Chaos more powerful than the aelementor's disdain for anything that cannot fly.

In battle, the Helonites are a force like no other. Favouring roving, ever-shifting vectors of attack, the Vanari and Hurakan of Helon work hand in hand to keep their enemies reeling and off balance. It is said that to face Helon upon the field of battle is to face a gale of killing shafts, to fight the ephemeral, to attempt to catch the air itself. Though they may lack the strength in depth that can be fielded by the Ymetricans, or the intense magical flair of the Zaitreci, they are unmatched in terms of mobility. It is a point of pride amongst the hosts of this Great Nation that few of their number fall to the enemy, even in massed battle. To the most extreme Helonite mindset, those who allow themselves to be caught by claw, blade or talon deserve to be weeded out, in any case.

ELLANIA AND ELLATHOR

The twins Ellania and Ellathor are prodigies, each reaching exceptional levels of skill in their chosen arts – physical combat in the case of Ellathor, and spellcraft in the case of his sister Ellania. Where they go, legends spring up in their wake – though that is not always something celebrated by their kin.

The Lumineth like to think of themselves as the incarnations of unalloyed excellence tempered by wisdom and experience. Though Ellania and Ellathor of Iliatha might lack the latter qualities, they possess the former in abundance. In showing their incredible gifts amongst their kin, they have earned as many enemies as friends, and though none will openly admit it, they have effectively been banished from their homeland as a result. So it is they wander the realms at large, fighting alongside not only the aelven people that sorely need their aid, but the other forces of civilisation as well.

Though comparatively young by aelven standards – a mere fifty years of age, in fact – the twins have risen high on the Teclian Ladder. A key tenet of the Lumineth mindset is to respect those who have achieved a higher state of enlightenment, no matter what their station in life. The twins undertook the hallucinogenic Trial of the Mindrazor before they had even reached physical maturity, only to pass with flying colours and even recommend changes that have since been widely adopted in all of the Ten Paradises. Word spread amongst the colleges of Hysh that a new benchmark of sheer capability had been set.

Watching their progress keenly, Teclis saw something of his younger self in Ellania. She had his steely confidence and natural aptitude with magic, and as far as he could ascertain, there was no limit to her potential. More astonishing than that, he saw an echo of his brother's exceptional skill in Ellathor. Already the twins were causing ripples in the high courts of the Lumineth, Ellania making her detractors look foolish time and time again in debating symposiums whilst Ellathor won Vanari duelling contests back to back. Their rising star put the established masters of their respective crafts in the shade.

The meteoric rise of the twins was to cast a long shadow, however, and when the implications of dark bargains began to circulate in the high courts, Teclis was swift to act. He came to the twins in person, bidding them visit each of the Ten Paradises in turn – and then, when they eventually returned, each of the Mortal Realms. In this way they would garner the perspective they needed to temper their raw ability. Should they survive, they would be amongst the greatest heroes the Lumineth had ever known. Teclis and Celennar, after a communion with Ellania, gifted the young mage the staff *Dianaer* to help her fulfil her potential. Tyrion, meanwhile, gifted Ellathor the aetherquartz sunblade *Altairi* from his godly armoury, reasoning that should the male twin show himself able to use its powers to the full, he will have proved his right to rule. Until that day, Ellania and Ellathor roam the Mortal Realms, never truly being one with the Lumineth – even when they fight on the same battlefield – but always striving to further the cause of order, justice, and enlightenment. If Teclis is correct in his divinations, the twins may one day change the fate of Hysh forever.

CHAMPIONS OF THE SCINARI

Collectively, the Scinari are the magocracy of Lumineth society. They embody the Teclian tradition, and hence strive to master the reflected, carefully shaped energies of magic and philosophy. Those who think these scholars weak are true fools, for the Scinari can kill their enemies in a hundred different ways, and do not hesitate to do so.

SCINARI CALLIGRAVES

The landscape is a canvas to the Scinari Calligrave. At the stroke of a brush, this symbol-mage can etch a vast runic sigil upon the wilderness. This will be a titanic version of a potent aelven rune that, through the power of geomantic transference, is seared from the Calligrave's enchanted parchments into the hard earth. In form it will be wrought to stabilise that which the power of Chaos may have put asunder. Yet when it is used upon the field of battle, it can disrupt and burn as well as becalm. Truly, for the Calligrave, the pen is mightier than the sword.

Pioneered by Il'yentai the Ancient, the pre-eminent scribe of Syar, the Calligrave's signature ability began as a technique by which a spell can be bound to a parchment for later release. It became a method by which a rune could be magnified in both scale and power, etched on a field near at hand by the transference magic of the Syari tradition. Held aloft from the land by stilt-like 'daethar' shoes so they could escape its solidity, the first Calligraves concentrated their art purely upon the realms themselves, often to quieten earthquakes and becalm landslides. Through necessity,

however, their skills came to be used as a weapon. Where the forces of Chaos sought to despoil and corrupt, the Calligraves would forcibly restore sanctity, their magic burning the flesh of the unhallowed even as it purified the land. Only later did they discover that, by painting with liquid light-magic siphoned from their aetherquartz lanterns, they could diminish enemy sorceries by evoking runes of nullification, paint wounds that spontaneously appeared on their foes, or even erase enemies from existence with the ease an artist might thumb away an errant stroke of charcoal.

SCINARI LORESEEKERS

Loreseekers straddle the two sides of Hyshian philosophy, and are expert wielders of the blade as well as magic. Though they hail from the Scinari caste, they strive to master the arts of the Vanari in their wanderings – a Loreseeker is all things Lumineth, it is said, in a single body and soul. Itinerant agents of Hysh quite used to fighting on their own, they wander the realms at will, supremely confident of their abilities. When channelling the moon, they embody the mysterious power of Teclian spellcasting, a match for any other Scinari sage. When attuning themselves to the sun, they move with the alacrity and speed of thought that typifies the Tyrionic tradition. Their given role is to hunt down the most obscure lore of the realms, unearthing that which has been forgotten in order to better serve the agenda of the Great Nations. Yet there is a darker side to their duty. The Loreseeker is sent to obscure and deny as well as reveal, sequestering those relics and treatises that may fall into the hands of the lesser races and hence cause untold damage. For every Loreseeker that acts as an ambassador in the wider realms, there is one whose role is closer to that of the vandal, or even the assassin.

VANARI LORD REGENTS

The Vanari are the cold, steel blade of the Lumineth, their determination unwavering and their skills in battle honed to a fine point. At the head of each host rides the Lord Regent, a magnificent sight as they blaze with energy on their lightcourser, blade raised in challenge as they race towards the heart of the enemy horde.

A blur of colour and light as they streak across the battlefield, the commanders of the Vanari hosts appear as the heroes of myth given life anew. A Lord Regent is the exemplar of the Tyrionic tradition, prizing skill at arms, charisma and swiftness of thought over quiet contemplation and the arcane arts. They are Tyrion's seconds in matters diplomatic, and speak with his voice in the debates and councils of the Teclian nations – under the right circumstances, a word from a Lord Regent can veto an entire invasion plan or send a hundred thousand Lumineth to war. In truth, the Lord Regent would prefer not to be embroiled in the endless debates and symposiums of the high courts – the intrigues, complexities and double meanings of these Teclian forums come dangerously close to wasted time in the eyes of one born into the Tyrionic tradition. These warriors are only really at home on the training field, the strategist's hall, and the white-hot crucible of battle. There, they come alive, exultant in the sheer skill and talent that has seen them rise from a role in the Vanari infantry, to the esoteric order of the Bladelords, and then finally to the command of an entire warhost, aelementiri temples and all.

To be named Lord Regent, an aspirant must undergo and survive a series of tests of worthiness devised by Tyrion himself. One of these is to travel to Haixiah and return enlightened, an odyssey that is never easily achieved. Another is to outwit and capture a lightcourser, one of the swift-footed quadrupeds that gallop across the northernmost reaches of the inner nations. So agile and active are these beasts it is said they never rest, and that they are living dynamos energized rather than tired out by their own exertions. Even when their riders wish to remain stationary they paw the ground and pad on the spot, anxious to get moving once more. They hate to be tethered, and are usually allowed to roam and circle as they will – so strong is the bond between steed and master they will never forsake their rider, and will always come at the Lord Regent's clarion-clear summons.

When wounded, lightcoursers can regenerate at great speed provided they are in direct sunlight, healing grievous injuries in an incredibly short period of time. Though they are not naturally fierce, they can deliver a powerful kick at whiplash speed, bowling over those who would bar their path so they can sprint on unhindered. So fast are they that, at full tilt, they can cross from one side of a battle to the other in a matter of seconds, their riders taking command or reinforcing a weakened flank whenever their soldiers appear outmatched. Lightcoursers can even keep up with the famously sleek and speedy treerunners employed by the Hurakan temples. It is said that it is easier to catch an arrow than it is to prevent a Lord Regent from reaching the crux point of a battle.

The Lord Regents themselves are expert riders, their shields deflecting arrows and robbing the power from brutish assaults even as their shining swords leap left and right to dispatch enemies with elegant, considered blows. With a few well-chosen thrusts, they can change the flow of a conflict completely. Armour is little defence against them, for the Lord Regents are also masters at channelling the energies of Hysh into the sunmetal. With a few whispered words of power, they can transform their blades and those of their warriors into weapons of pure light that are able to pierce both flesh and plate armour with barely any resistance.

LYRIOR UTHRALLE, VOICE OF THE LORD PHOENIX

No normal commander is Lyrior Uthralle, for he speaks with the authority of Tyrion himself. Uthralle is the Lord Regent Supreme, the figurehead for the Tyrionic nations and spokesperson for their interests whenever the great and the good of their Teclian equivalents debate the future of the realms. He has a reputation for being cool-headed and logical, even amongst the Lumineth, but in truth it is a carefully maintained mask. When in private, and in total surety he is alone, Uthralle screams into the void – even with a trio of personal Scinari Cathallars to provide him catharsis on a daily basis, it is the only way he can truly calm his soul. In saving the vital Ymetrican citadel of Tor Limina from a Flesh-eater invasion at Tyrion's express behest, Uthralle had to abandon his home city of Muavheil to the juggernaut of Waaagh! Gorondrog. Upon his return he found only smoking ruins. He still blames himself for the death of his kin, and wept bitter tears when he finally uncovered the remains of his young family. Those closest to him believe that Uthralle's steely sense of duty is the only thing stopping him abandoning his post altogether and dedicating his life to the eradication of all the savage races across Hysh's great span.

VANARI BANNERBLADES

The position of Bannerblade is earned only through demonstrating utmost dependability, for the standards they bear to war are incredibly valuable, enchanted and blessed by mages from each type of aelementiri shrine, the better to embody the balance sought after by all Realm-lords.

The majestic standards borne by Vanari Bannerblades are woven from solarsilk, a material that catches rays of power from the Hyshian sun whilst letting wind, rain and snow pass through as if the fabric were made of no more than light. Though incredibly difficult to work with, it is almost weightless, closer to a projected image than a physical material. The artifice of the Syari ensures these 'world banners' are sown with sacred imagery and symbols of aelven supremacy. Foremost amongst these icons is that of the Eclipsian, a figure of purity and symmetry that has pride of place at the banner's heart. It symbolises the coming together of the solar and lunar philosophies of Hysh, blending the two elements together. There are those in Lumineth society that believe Tyrion and Teclis were once one being, and that they will one day become a single entity again, embodying the Eclipsian and reaching the true zenith of aelven potential. Whether it is true, none can say, but the image has great power and resonance nonetheless – the same icon graces the top of the Loreseeker's staff, for they too seek balance between the teachings associated with the sun and the moon.

It is not just the dichotomy of sun and moon that the banner embodies, but also the aelementiri disciplines, the runes of which appear above the Eclipsian. As such it is inspiring to all Lumineth who fight around it – and not just on a spiritual level. When its guardian speaks a sacred word of power, the Hyshian energies it harnesses beam out from the banner with the intensity of a new dawn, dazzling the enemy whilst invigorating nearby Lumineth and making the Bannerblade themselves seem to glow from within like some numinous angel.

To allow a world banner to fall is unthinkable to the one who bears it; the very idea of such a radiant and resplendent artefact falling into the bloody muck of the battlefield is enough to make a Bannerblade shudder with revulsion. So it is that all those who hold this office are experts in a form of swordsmanship called Ollirathai, a term that roughly translates into the Azyrite tongue as the Shield of Swords. With his back foot planted fast, the Bannerblade can fence half a dozen enemies to a standstill whilst keeping the standard held immovable, his sunmetal sword whipping, darting, impaling and disarming the foe one by one until the threat is neutralised. Should the worst come to pass and the banner fall, its bearer will go into exile, seeking to burn the weakness from their soul by walking into the transformative light of Hysh's Perimeter Inimical. As yet, none who have done so have returned.

VANARI BLADELORDS

It is said that in the art of the blade, there are none deadlier than the Vanari Bladelords. Mind, body and soul is bent towards the perfection of the swordforms they practise from dawn till dusk. Their swords are sharp enough to cut a hair along its length, but it is their order's cold, irrefutable logic that is their deadliest weapon.

In terms of Lumineth culture, the Vanari Bladelords are walking contradictions. Their order hails from the Tyrionic nations of Hysh; being Vanari, they lean towards matters military rather than philosophical. Yet they have made their home in the Teclian nations, and bear the icon of the Scinari as an honour marking. They study cause and effect in fractal complexity at the high spires of the most learned aelves; in return, on the field of war, they act as guardians for the mages and mystics of their people.

It is the aspiration of many high-ranking Vanari to master the art of wielding a sunmetal blade. Some maintain this is to better cut short those conflicts they are forced to undergo, in the name of swift victory, whilst others admit they do so to achieve self-actualisation, but none would say that it was for the frisson of the kill well delivered. They are master artisans, and take a quiet pride in their work; a Bladelord is never boastful or self-aggrandising, instead letting their sword speak on their behalf. In battle, they do not speak at all. Their entire consciousness is bent towards thinking through the likely combinations of momentum, aggression, speed, dexterity and mass that will inform the exchange of violence to come. A hundred equations of cause and effect, blending and unravelling with unconscious ease, ensure the Bladelord's edge cuts through the guard and armour of their opponent to strike a blow swift and true. The foe's axe comes in hard, but the Bladelord is no longer there, having stepped alongside his mark to cut head from neck and allow the decapitated body to stumble on. A kick to the knee of the next enemy as he rushes past and the blade cuts his spine wide open as he falls. A third screams, lunging with a jagged spear, only to impale himself on a blade that was not there a split second before. Smoothly the sword withdraws, and the Bladelord stands ready once more amongst the corpses.

Arrayed for battle, the Bladelords, are an impressive sight. They wear the ancestral helms of their order and the elegant back-banners they earn upon passing the stringent tests of mind and body that mark them as fully fledged members of their organisation. They bear no normal weapons, but sunmetal greatblades etched with the ancient aelven runes of strength, honour and irrefutable law. Some of the leaders of each collective wield dual blades marked with runes of doom – though slender, these can open a foe's throat in an eye-blink. Even the greatblades used by the majority of this warrior elite are lightweight given their size and length, each so impeccably balanced they can slice through armour with the right momentum behind them.

The swordform practised by the Bladelords is replete with swirling, swooping gestures, all timed to trace a lethal journey through the ranks of the enemy. The aelves' reaction speed, bolstered by their intense concentration and ability to predict the nuances of battle from a hundred different cues, enables them to cut arrows from the sky a moment before impact. When faced with a charging horde, they will whirl their blades in great figures of eight that interweave along the line to form a wall of slicing steel that swiftly dismembers lesser opponents. More imposing foes will instead be read for any signs of weakness or clues to their attack style. With the perfect countermeasure worked out, a Bladelord will make a single strike – but it is invariably a lethal one.

YLIANA, THE WHITE MANTIS

The Bladelord champion Yliana has a reaction speed so fast she seems to blur in the heat of battle. She is said to have slain shard-scorpions in her infancy using nothing more than a cooking knife, waiting for the hideous creatures to attack before impaling them and yanking back her arm before their stingers could deliver their deadly toxin. As an adult, she has left such one-sided challenges behind, and looks back on her youthful indulgences with shame. Now she kills only when absolutely necessary. Yet as the powers of Chaos seem set to overwhelm reality itself, the act of slaughter in the name of reason has meant the blood upon her blades has rarely dried. She fights to protect the Scinari of Ymetrica as they pursue their ambitious agendas to bring order to the realms, and any who drive an attack towards the mages will be met by Yliana's weaving, spinning blades. At the end of each day, Yliana washes away the caked gore and filth of battle and meditates until her mind is cleansed once more, attaining a state of balance so that she can fight at full potential the next dawn. Only her closest comrades know that her composure is slowly starting to crack.

VANARI STARSHARD BALLISTAS

With barely a whisper the twin bolts of the Starshard ballista cut the air, leaving glowing traces of Hyshian magic in their wake. A second later they impale their targets, blood spraying from near-symmetrical wounds as the secondary effect of the bolts unleashes a burst of dazzling light in the foe's ranks.

The Lumineth prize speed and accuracy over ponderous, indiscriminate destruction, a fact borne out even in their most widely used field weapon – the Starshard ballista. This artillery piece is light in construction, made from supple yet extremely strong wood harvested from the spear-straight dreamwood trees dotting the wildernesses of the Great Nations. In form it is something like an enlarged version of the many-stringed compound bows of the Auralan Sentinels, mounted upon an elegant tripod that allows it to swivel to draw a bead on a range of targets. Each Starshard launches a pair of long-shafted, perfectly balanced bolts that streak across the battlefield, painting the air with twin trails of intense white light as they do so. The artillerists that crew these machines are selected from those Auralan Sentinels with the sharpest eyesight and steadiest hands; given priority targets by the Lord Regent in command of their battery, the crew of the ballista pick the right moment for a clear shot before pulling the trigger. A moment later, the twin bolts impale their target as one, invariably killing the foe instantly.

Yet that is not the end of the impact these inventive projectiles have upon the battle. When shaken by the sudden halt, the oval reservoirs of aetherquartz-infused water that sit behind each bolt-tip emit a sudden and blinding light. This can send adversaries around the immediate target into disarray, their vision blurring or even stolen entirely by the sudden burst of illumination.

That same concept is employed in the aetherquartz lanterns that are planted in the ground around the ballista – should an enemy approach too close, these lanterns will blaze with dazzling light to rob the impact of the charge and allow the Vanari to evade long enough for reinforcements to arrive.

'*H*old,' said Aaralia. 'Hold fire.' Darai-Thoq picked up her lover's measured and soft voice even over the cacophony of battle. Aaralia's sunmetal blade was raised, its tip pointed right at the face of a charging, bellowing gargant so massive he would soon blot out the setting sun entirely. 'On my mark,' said Aaralia, as composed as if she were delivering a lecture on warfare in the spires of Settler's Gain. Calm was vital; this all Vanari knew. Then the gargant's stink reached Darai-Thoq like a slap in the face, and her eyes narrowed. It stamped a human-built wall flat, elbowing over a tower on its rampage towards them. 'Now,' said Aaralia, whipping her blade downwards. Darai-Thoq took the shot, twin bolts flying from the Starshard in blurs of light. They struck the gargant at the same time, one arrow thunking home in each of its eye sockets. A perfect double shot. Even as it toppled backwards, Aaralia smoothly reloaded the ballista. A second later her blade was levelled at a new gargant. 'Hold,' she said again. 'Hold fire…'

UPON THE KILLING WINDS OF HYSH

Hair whipping in the wind, bright colours blurring with sheer velocity, the Hurakan race around the flanks of the battle to send arrow and spell lancing into the enemy's ranks. Masters of death from afar, they are inescapable, for they ride the winds themselves and are just as difficult to pin down.

The Hurakan are at one with the wind, whether calming breeze, howling gale or raging cyclone. Their temples are constantly buffeted by strong air currents and ring to the strange music of the skies. These structures are built into the floating metaliths that can be found across the Mortal Realms and are favoured highly by wind spirits of all kinds, especially when they form clusters or airborne archipelagos for the invisible entities to race through. Aspirants to the Hurakan way of life will make their way to such places by mastering a trance-like state, known as hurathré, that enables slow levitation. Once they have ascended to the metalith they seek, they erect shrines upon it, even in the face of the perilous gusts and scouring sandstorms that the native winds send to test them.

In time, a Hurakan shrine will be strung with chimes and holes will be drilled with awls along its length so the winds that whirl past it give rise to melodious chords and tinkling percussion. If a wind finds the music pleasing, it will frequent that site, and in doing so begin to form a bond with the Hurakan aspirants that praise it and sing to it as it rushes by. Then, when they believe they have found an accord with the spirit of the wind, an aspirant will throw themselves from the edge of the metalith. If the wind chooses them, it will catch them up and send them soaring through the skies in a spiritual breakthrough that fills their soul with heady elation. If it spurns them, they will instead plummet to their death. Such is the risk a Lumineth takes when they seek to bond with the spirits of Hysh, but those who are deemed worthy inherit powers that elevate them far above mortal capability.

HURAKAN WINDMAGES

Hurakan Windmages are the wisest and most gifted of all their monastic order, those who have formed a symbiotic bond with the winds of their homeland to such an extent they consider one another family. These aelementiri feel more at home in the sky than on the earth; to a Windmage, the act of walking on the ground feels as strange and anachronistic as the act of crawling like an infant on all fours feels to an adult. Instead they go about the lands borne upon an aelementor wind, visible as a blur of energy and roiling form, that carries them high and far at will.

The bond between a Windmage and their aelementor is spiritual, but also one of practical mutual benefit. The Windmage, for their part, gets a potent and nigh-immortal ally with which to further the agenda of the Lumineth. In return, the wind aelementor is able to travel to places which it might otherwise never explore; to these excitable and curious entities, moving from one realm to another is a wondrous opportunity to gust and rage across brand-new landscapes. Likewise, without a physical link to reality, its sentience might disperse, leaving it no more than a scattering of kinetic energy. However, with a Windmage – or more specifically, their aspiragillum wand – forming a focal point, the aelementor can remain whole and focused almost indefinitely. Some are even strong and determined enough to take a physical incarnation. Provided the aspiragillum keeps spinning, the wind will keep blowing and have a surety of purpose. Should the sacred artefact stop its revolutions, the wind will lose its focus and perhaps be lost forever. As such, if a Windmage is slain, his disciples will do everything in their power to reclaim the sacred artefact and bear it back to the aerial temple frequented by that wind.

HARANTIO, THE GALERIDER OF HELON COREWARD

Harantio, called the Galerider by those who have heard his legend, is a Hurakan mage hundreds of years old. He is a popular figure in Helonite folklore, in particular because of his famous luck – which, as all delighted youngsters know, is in truth the giggling wind spirit Parashei. The Tale of the Crimson Orbs, for instance, tells of how he stole the fist-sized rubies prized by Groggo the Shark-Eater, and then escaped when the Mega-Gargant 'inexplicably' tripped on the carcass of his own meal and impaled himself on a Stegadon skull. The Tale of the Long-sought Soul tells of the time the Galerider angered Sigmar by stealing one of his storms, later to be struck by lightning and fall from the skies when crossing the tempestuous Temeritis Ocean. He 'somehow' drifted into the secret sanctum of Scuala the Myrmai, the lost daughter of Prince Motlai, and awakened to find the love of his life peering down at him. Harantio laughs in the face of adversity; when his enemies fire their arrows at him, he deflects them with a wave of his calligraphed fan – it is Parashei who does the work of redirection, of course, just as it is Parashei who sends his foes flying left and right at the slightest tap of Harantio's aspiragillum wand. The tales always end in the same way, of course; driven ever onwards by his insatiable wanderlust, the Galerider always leaves the site of his victory to find new adventure over the horizon. Though none know if Harantio truly exists, there are several reports of a mysterious Hurakan figure bringing victory to the beleaguered Lumineth when it seems the forces of darkness are on the brink of victory.

HURAKAN WINDCHARGERS

It is said that when the Windchargers set eyes upon their prey, there can be no survival for their mark. Wherever the wind races strong, their arrows strike with lethal force. Where the wind is impossible to catch, its hunters are impossible to evade. They fire not volleys as do the Auralan Sentinels, arcing their shafts in synchrony into the mass of the enemy army, but instead loose the killing shots of the sniper, each missile striking with pinpoint precision to kill a high-value target. One arrow, one kill – that is the creed of the Windcharger, and they excel at making it a reality.

The key to the uncanny skill of these archers is their bond with the winds that form their aelementors. When their shot is loosed, it will be carried to its destination by the wind itself, giving it a supernatural degree of accuracy over and above the natural excellence of the marksman that fires it. It can curve around obstacles, dart through arrow slits in a fortress gatehouse, or pierce the gaps in a shieldwall to find the eye sockets of those sheltering behind. In the process, the arrow is accelerated to the speed of a bullet. It is common for such a shot to tear the head from its target rather than simply piercing them, striking with the force of a ballista-launched spear.

Even the deadliest archer, of course, cannot lay low his mark without first hunting him down. This is where the steed known as the Hyshian treerunner comes into play, a long-limbed beast that sprints with the wind purely for the joy of it. Named for the fact they can even run through forest canopies by leaping nimbly from bough to bough, treerunners have a natural aptitude in judging the passage of air currents, allowing them to make truly impressive leaps as they are buoyed up by gusts of wind. To the uninitiated, it seems like they are all but immune to the pull of gravity; they can scale cliff faces and towers with a series of perfectly timed jumps. Should a Hurakan rider tame one of these creatures, usually with the subtlety and beauty of the melody he uses to soothe its skittish soul, it will bear him across the shattered wildernesses of the Mortal Realms with the ease of a passing zephyr.

In battle, treerunner and rider alike move around the enemy with matchless grace, making it extremely difficult to land a telling blow. The enemy stumbles and lurches as his strikes find nothing but air, kept off balance with kicks and pushes that expose him for a killing shot. The riders carry a blade as a concession to tradition more than as a practical weapon; in spirit, they forsake the sword entirely when they take up the sacred bow of their order. The Hurakan instead practise a martial form where they use their exceptional archery skills at point-blank range with incredible dexterity. The dormancy of the blade is a small sacrifice, given that a single shot from a Hurakan archer can tear a foe's limb from his body in a streak of blood.

THE GALE MADE MANIFEST

The air howls as a Spirit of the Wind takes physical form, borne aloft by a tornado of exceptional strength. From its greatbow fly killing shafts that pick out the enemy's leaders even as the gale of its rage snatches away their commands. To land a solid blow upon such a lithe and nimble entity is all but impossible.

In its core state, a Hyshian wind is a mercurial force that whips across the lands when the realm's solar radiance waxes. The strongest of these entities possess a fierce animus, and are given names by the aelves in an attempt to know them and predict where they will wreak destruction next. Many are violent and cruel, flattening burgeoning towns or tearing new buildings into the skies to dash them back down miles away. Long ago, these spirits may have been warm, playful and capricious, tousling the meadows and trees of their native lands and refreshing those who walked amongst them. Since the Age of Chaos, however, they have grown resentful and fierce. They claim swathes of territory as their own, tracing the same paths year on year or spiralling in grand cyclonic tours that carve across oceans and batter coastlines.

The natural state of such winds is ephemeral and invisible, though since the Reinvention there have been some that have taken physical forms. Given cohesion by the mages that take sacred masks from their temples and use them as focal points, these aelementors are known as the Spirits of the Wind.

When roused to war, a Spirit of the Wind coalesces much as a tornado, then binds tight into a physical manifestation of that wind's essence. It is common for them to echo the lithe form of the Horned Fox, a semi-mythical beast of Hysh that is sly, swift and famously impossible to catch. They are surrounded at all times by a tearing, swirling vortex; when they scour their way across the battlefield in a blur of dust and glimmering Hyshian magic, this whirlwind sweeps up those in their path and hurls them away to break on the stony ground. Some possess mischievous temperaments, reaching out to turn helmets or whip the cloaks of the proud around their heads so they cannot see, but when their ire is raised they use the same tactics to throttle and blind. Some snatch the very air from their victims' mouths, asphyxiating them in a matter of seconds or, conversely, fill their airways with gale-force winds until their lungs burst. The most blunt and forthright will simply dash the enemy's heads open on sharp rocks, bear them over cliffs, or drive them onto the drawn blades of their comrades. Yet even these spirits will attack at a distance whenever possible.

It is unheard of for a Spirit of the Wind to stay in one place for long; should one be grounded or bound to one site, it would swiftly go insane. As such, Spirits of the Wind avoid physical contact as much as possible, instead firing spear-length shafts from their greatbows and guiding the arrows towards the eyes, hearts and throats of their victims. So swift are they that several such killing shots can be launched in blurring succession. Even as the rank and file are tossed like rag dolls by the violence of the cyclone, the officers of the enemy army are put down with pinpoint precision.

SEVIRETH, LORD OF THE SEVENTH WIND

There are said to be seven regal winds in Hysh. Immortal and unstoppable, they go where they may, and will never be bound to another's will. Yet there is one amongst them that has suffered so much that it has been driven to the edge of madness. That creature is known as the Scourer, the Red Gale and the Killing Sandstorm, but to the Realm-lords it is Sevireth.

Sevireth once blew wild and free across the Desert of Illuminations in Haixiah, a trackless swathe of land that glittered beautifully when the light of Hysh waxed, and glowed like a soft and lambent sea under the gaze of its true moon. He taught the mysteries of the crystal desert to those stylites brave enough to fast on the meditation spires under the baking radiance of Hysh, and conferred the power of flight upon the most worthy. When Slaanesh inveigled his tendrils into Lumineth society – and that of the Sigmarite humans who sought to learn from them – the deserts were prowled by agents of Chaos as well as the seekers of true knowledge. It was a sect of Slaaneshi cultists that entrapped Sevireth, their intent to neutralise a potent ally of those who would one day become the Realm-lords. They did so by luring him into a network of volcanic caves, shaped under the supervision of their Infernal Enrapturess patron so that when a wind passed through their hollows it created the most beautiful music. Once entranced, they sealed the caves with boulders that fit as snugly as corks in bottles, and left the wind to rage impotently inside.

It was Teclis that set free the desert wind after the time of the Reinvention. Sevireth flew from the mouth of that cave network in a terrifying rage; not the indiscriminate anger of a wounded beast, but that of a proud king who has been humiliated. Since that day he has sought to slay all those who might harm Hysh. No playful zephyr is he, but a searing, screaming sandstorm that scours flesh from bone and erodes the statues of tyrants to bland nothingness with the intensity of its passing. Those struck by his arrows are caught up in vortexes of flame, and those who hear his half-mad howl are haunted for the rest of their days. Even the other winds fear his anger – and rightly so.

The purple, gold and white of Zaitrec shines out even amid the muck and squalor of a skaven lair. Their assault is like an enchanted blade driven deep into the body of the enemy swarm.

LIGHT INCARNATE

The Lumineth array themselves for war in great splendour. When they gather close, their innate magical auras blend together into a radiance that can dazzle or even blind their foes. Here we present a showcase of Lumineth Realm-lords miniatures expertly painted by the 'Eavy Metal team and Design Studio army painters.

Sevireth is the rage of the desert gale, tearing at the foe with sudden sandstorms whilst sending killing shafts into the hearts of those who would darken and despoil the realms.

Hurakan Windmage

Ellania and Ellathor, Eclipsian Warsages

Sevireth, Lord of the Seventh Wind

Lyrior Uthralle, Warden of Ymetrica

Scinari Calligrave

Hurakan Windcharger

Vanari Bannerblade

Vanari Lord Regent

Myari Lightcaller

Ailenn,
the Mind's Edge

Bahannar

Senaela

Myari's Purifiers

The wind-borne arrows of the Hurakan eliminate choice targets as Auralan Sentinels loft volley after volley into the packed ranks behind. Even a daemonic assault cannot shake the Realm-lords' nerve and determination for long.

To witness the Vanari of Zaitrec in battle is to see a masterclass in precision and skill. Yet this Great Nation is famed more for its magic than its martial prowess; shining bright with Hyshian energy, their massed exorcisms can banish even the most powerful Nighthaunt.

Scinari Loreseeker

Vanari Bladelord
Seneschal of Iliatha

Vanari Bladelord
of Alumnia

Vanari Bladelord
of Helon

Vanari Starshard Ballista

THE ARMIES OF THE REALM-LORDS

This section of *Broken Realms: Teclis* contains a major update to the first edition of *Battletome: Lumineth Realm-lords*. It adds to the book the warscrolls and allegiance abilities for Hurakan units, new warscrolls and allegiance abilities for Vanari and Scinari units, and the scenery warscroll for the Shrine Luminor terrain feature.

ALLEGIANCE ABILITIES

This section contains new and expanded allegiance abilities for Lumineth Realm-lords armies. The rules for using allegiance abilities can be found in the *Warhammer Age of Sigmar Core Book*.

LUMINETH REALM-LORDS

Abilities available to every unit in a Lumineth Realm-lords army (pg 125).

VANARI, SCINARI AND HURAKAN

Additional battle traits, command traits and artefacts of power available to VANARI, SCINARI and HURAKAN units in a Lumineth Realm-lords army (pg 126-128).

SPELL LORES

Spells available to TECLIS and HURAKAN WIZARDS in a Lumineth Realm-lords army (pg 129).

SHRINE LUMINOR

The rules and scenery warscroll for a new terrain feature that can be taken as part of a Lumineth Realm-lords army (pg 130-131).

GREAT NATIONS

Abilities for two of the Lumineth Great Nations from the Tyrionic hemisphere of Hysh (pg 132-133). These rules can be used by units in a Lumineth Realm-lords army that have been given the appropriate keyword (see the Lumineth Great Nations battle trait, opposite).

BATTLEPLANS

This section includes a new narrative battleplan (pg 134) that can be played with a Lumineth Realm-lords army.

PATH TO GLORY

This section contains rules for using your Lumineth Realm-lords collection in Path to Glory campaigns (pg 136-139).

WARSCROLLS

This section includes warscrolls for the Lumineth Realm-lords miniatures released alongside *Broken Realms: Teclis*. There are two types of warscroll included in this section:

WARSCROLL BATTALIONS

These are formations made up of several Lumineth Realm-lords units that combine their strengths to gain powerful new abilities (pg 140-141).

WARSCROLLS

A warscroll for each new unit is included here. The rules for using the unit, along with its characteristics and abilities, are detailed on its warscroll (pg 142-151).

PITCHED BATTLE PROFILES

This section contains Pitched Battle profiles for the units and warscroll battalions in this section, as well as those for the units and warscrolls battalions from the Battletome Updates section earlier in this book (pg 152).

ALLEGIANCE ABILITIES
LUMINETH REALM-LORDS

BATTLE TRAITS – POWER OF THE LUMINETH

AETHERQUARTZ RESERVE

Every Lumineth Realm-lord carries with them a tiny reserve of aetherquartz that they keep in a gem-like container. In extremis, the Realm-lord can break the vessel's seal, allowing them to temporarily increase their physical and arcane prowess, albeit at a heavy emotional cost.

Each unit in a Lumineth Realm-lords army starts the battle with 1 aetherquartz reserve. Once per phase, you can say that 1 unit will use its aetherquartz reserve to use 1 of the following aetherquartz reserve abilities. However, if you do so, subtract 1 from that unit's Bravery characteristic for the rest of the battle.

Heightened Reflexes: You can say that a unit will use this ability when it is picked to be the target of an enemy attack. If you do so, add 1 to save rolls for attacks that target that unit until the end of that phase.

Heightened Senses: You can say that a unit will use this ability when it is picked to shoot or fight. If you do so, add 1 to hit rolls for attacks made by that unit until the end of that phase.

Magical Boost: You can say that a unit will use this ability after it has attempted to cast a spell but before any unbinding rolls are made for that spell. If you do so, you can either add 1 to that casting roll or re-roll that casting roll.

Magical Insight: You can say that a unit will use this ability at the start of your hero phase. If you do so, that unit can attempt to cast 1 extra spell in that phase.

ABSORB DESPAIR

Scinari Cathallars can assuage the dark despair that afflicts a Lumineth Realm-lord after the use of their aetherquartz reserve. The negative energies are not just burned off but released towards the foe as a psychological weapon.

If a friendly unit uses its aetherquartz reserve while it is wholly within 18" of any friendly **CATHALLARS**, you can pick 1 of the **CATHALLARS** within 18" of that unit and say that they will absorb the negative energy. A **CATHALLAR** cannot absorb negative energy more than once per phase.

If a **CATHALLAR** absorbs the negative energy from a friendly unit, do not subtract 1 from that unit's Bravery characteristic. Instead, you can pick 1 enemy unit within 18" of that **CATHALLAR**. If you do so, subtract 1 from the Bravery characteristic of that enemy unit for the rest of the battle. The same enemy unit cannot be affected by this ability more than once per battle.

LIGHTNING REACTIONS

Lumineth Realm-lords possess a natural skill and talent that far outstrips that of most other races. When combined with decades of martial training, this creates a warrior elite that can think faster, act more decisively and fight more proficiently than any other.

During the combat phase, when it is your turn to pick a unit to fight, you can pick 2 eligible units instead of 1. If you do so, each of those units can fight one after the other in the order of your choice.

Designer's Note: *This ability only applies to units that fight **during** the combat phase; therefore, it cannot be used for units that fight at the start or the end of the combat phase, or for units that fight in any phase other than the combat phase.*

LUMINETH GREAT NATIONS

The Lumineth are gathered into Great Nations, each with their own unique culture, specialisations and sets of social mores.

When you choose a Lumineth Realm-lords army, you can give it a Great Nation keyword from the list below. All **LUMINETH REALM-LORDS** units in your army gain that keyword, and you can use the allegiance abilities listed for that Great Nation on the page indicated.

- **ALUMNIA** (pg 132)
- **HELON** (pg 133)
- **YMETRICA** (see *Battletome: Lumineth Realm-lords*)
- **SYAR** (see *Battletome: Lumineth Realm-lords*)
- **ILIATHA** (see *Battletome: Lumineth Realm-lords*)
- **ZAITREC** (see *Battletome: Lumineth Realm-lords*)

If a model already has a Great Nation keyword on its warscroll, it cannot gain another one. This does not preclude you from including the unit in your army, but you cannot use the allegiance abilities for its Great Nation.

VANARI

BATTLE TRAITS – WARRIORS OF LIGHT

SHINING COMPANY

Vanari warriors often fight in a tight grouping, so close that their shoulders or stirrups are almost touching. This densely packed formation sacrifices a little fluidity but combines the bright light of each numinous soul into a dazzling brilliance that befuddles enemies.

After a **VANARI** unit is set up, if the base of each model in the unit is touching the bases of 2 or more other models from the same unit, then that unit becomes a shining company.

That unit remains a shining company until, after finishing a move, the base of each model in the unit is no longer touching the bases of 2 or more other models from the same unit, or until, after removing a slain model from the unit, the bases of any remaining models in the unit are not touching the bases of 2 or more other models from the same unit.

Subtract 1 from hit rolls for attacks that target a shining company. However, a shining company cannot run or charge, and models in that unit can only move 1" when they pile in.

COMMAND TRAITS – LORDS OF THE WARHOSTS
VANARI generals only.

D3	Command Trait
1	**Grand Strategist:** *This general carefully prepares before every battle to ensure that they have every advantage over their foes.* If this general is on the battlefield at the start of the first battle round, you receive 1 extra command point.
2	**Consummate Warrior:** *This general is a master of the blade.* Once per turn, you can re-roll 1 hit roll or 1 wound roll for an attack made by this general, or 1 save roll for an attack that targets this general.
3	**Astute Commander:** *This general is expert at reading the flow of battle. Few opportunities to capitalise on success escape their notice.* If this general is on the battlefield, each time you spend a command point, roll a dice. On a 6, you receive 1 command point.

ARTEFACTS OF POWER – GIFTS OF THE SUN
VANARI HEROES only.

D3	Artefact of Power
1	**Syari Pommel:** *This fashionable pommel is crafted from beautifully etched aetherquartz, which at need can be spent by the bearer in battle.* The bearer starts the battle with 1 extra aetherquartz reserve.
2	**Senlui Amulet:** *This amulet bestows great swiftness to the wearer when their fingertip is traced along the elegant rune graven upon it.* The bearer can run and still charge in the same turn.
3	**Sun Stone:** *The brilliant rays that radiate from this talisman can rapidly disperse hostile magic.* The bearer can attempt to dispel 1 endless spell at the start of your hero phase in the same manner as a **WIZARD**, and attempt to unbind 1 spell in the enemy hero phase in the same manner as a **WIZARD**. If the bearer is already a **WIZARD**, add 1 to the first dispelling and unbinding roll you make for them each phase.

SCINARI

BATTLE TRAITS – MASTERS OF THE TECLAMENTARI

DEEP THINKERS

The Scinari are renowned across the realms for their profound knowledge and thoughtful deliberation. Given time, there are few arcane rituals that a Scinari cannot master.

At the start of your hero phase, you can pick any friendly **SCINARI WIZARDS** and declare that instead of casting any spells in that phase they will contemplate (you can have some contemplate while others attempt to cast spells). If you do so, in your next hero phase, when a friendly **SCINARI WIZARD** that contemplated in your last hero phase attempts to cast its first spell in the current hero phase, it is automatically cast with a casting roll of 9 that cannot be modified (do not roll 2D6), but it can be unbound.

COMMAND TRAITS – LORDS OF BRILLIANCE
SCINARI generals only.

D3	Command Trait
1	**Spellmaster:** *This general has studied the arcane arts for centuries.* Once in each of your hero phases, you can re-roll 1 failed casting roll for this general.
2	**Loremaster:** *Few can rival this general's knowledge of aelven magic.* This general knows 1 extra spell from the Lore of Hysh (see *Battletome: Lumineth Realm-lords*).
3	**Warmaster:** *This general has mastered advanced strategies and tactics of battle.* If this general is part of your army and on the battlefield at the start of your hero phase, roll a dice. On a 4+, you receive 1 extra command point.

ARTEFACTS OF POWER – HEIRLOOMS OF HYSH
SCINARI only.

D3	Artefact of Power
1	**Phoenix Stone:** *This ancient crystal can heal those on the brink of death.* If a friendly **LUMINETH REALM-LORDS HERO** is slain within 12" of the bearer, before removing that model from play, roll a dice. On a 6, that model is not slain, all wounds allocated to it are healed and any wounds that currently remain to be allocated to it or its unit are negated.
2	**Silver Wand:** *This slender wand is covered with winding Lumineth runes.* The bearer can attempt to cast 1 extra spell in your hero phase.
3	**Blade of Leaping Gold:** *A more finely balanced blade than this has never been wrought.* Pick 1 of the bearer's melee weapons. Add 3 to the Attacks characteristic of that weapon.

HURAKAN

BATTLE TRAITS – KINDRED OF THE WINDS

MOVE LIKE THE WIND

Hurakan warriors are almost impossible to pin down in combat. They swirl around their foes, first closing to strike, and then performing gravity-defying leaps to take them over or away from their enemies.

When you make a pile-in move with a **Hurakan** model, it does not have to finish the move at least as close to the nearest enemy model. In addition, when you make a pile-in move with a **Hurakan** model, if it made a charge move in the same turn, it can fly and can move an extra 3" when it piles in.

Designer's Note: *These rules allow* **Hurakan** *models to flow around enemy units in combat, and to back off from fights that do not favour them.*

COMMAND TRAITS – LORDS OF AIR
Hurakan Windmage generals only.

D3	Command Trait
1	**Grand Windrider:** *This general is an unrivalled leader of Windcharger formations.* Replace this general's Windleap ability with: 'If a friendly **Windchargers** unit starts a move wholly within 24" of this general, when it makes that move, that unit has a Move characteristic of 16" and can fly.'
2	**Swift:** *The speed at which this general loops and soars through the air has earned them great respect among their Hurakan peers.* Add 3" to this general's Move characteristic.
3	**Loremaster:** *Few can rival this general's knowledge of aelven magic.* If this general is a **Wizard**, they know 1 extra spell from the Lore of the Winds (pg 129).

ARTEFACTS OF POWER – GIFTS OF THE WINDS
Hurakan Windmages only.

D3	Artefact of Power
1	**Windblast Fan:** *With a flick of the bearer's wrist, this fan can project a great gust of air that drives back the foe.* Once per battle, at the start of the enemy movement phase, you can pick 1 enemy unit within 3" of the bearer. That unit must make a normal move and must retreat.
2	**Wind Stone:** *This clouded gem can be hurled with the force of a cannonball.* Once per battle in your shooting phase, you can pick 1 enemy unit within 18" of the bearer that is visible to them and roll a dice. On a 1, nothing happens. On a 2-4, that unit suffers 3 mortal wounds. On a 5+, that unit suffers D6 mortal wounds.
3	**Buffeting Aspiragillum:** *The unpredictable currents that swirl and gust around this wand can disrupt enemy attacks, both physical and arcane.* Roll a dice each time you allocate a wound or mortal wound to the bearer. On a 5+, that wound or mortal wound is negated.

SPELL LORES

You can choose or roll for one spell from the following table for each **Hurakan Wizard** in a Lumineth Realm-lords army. **Teclis** knows all of the spells from the following table.

LORE OF THE WINDS
Teclis and Hurakan Wizards only.

D6 Spell

1 **Freezing Squall:** *The caster invokes a vindictive, icy cold wind that chills the enemy to the bone and slows their advance to a crawl.*

Freezing Squall has a casting value of 5. If successfully cast, pick 1 enemy unit within 12" of the caster that is visible to them. That unit cannot run until your next hero phase.

2 **Howling Gale:** *The caster directs a gang of obstreperous currents towards a group of foes that make it impossible for them to hear commands.*

Howling Gale has a casting value of 7. If successfully cast, pick 1 enemy unit within 12" of the caster that is visible to them. That unit cannot use or benefit from command abilities until your next hero phase.

3 **Guiding Flurries:** *The wizard requests the aid of a gaggle of flurries that carry the Lumineth's arrows far across the field of battle in arcing trajectories, or else speed them in a straight line directly towards their target.*

Guiding Flurries has a casting value of 7. If successfully cast, pick 1 friendly **Lumineth Realm-lords** unit armed with missile weapons that is wholly within 12" of the caster and visible to them, then say if the spell lofts the missiles or directs the missiles.

If the spell lofts the missiles, until your next hero phase, add 6" to the Range characteristic of missile weapons used by that unit.

If the spell directs the missiles, until your next hero phase, add 1 to hit rolls for attacks made with missile weapons by that unit.

4 **Calming Zephyr:** *The caster coaxes forth a playful breeze that heals and calms those that have suffered injury.*

Calming Zephyr has a casting value of 6. If successfully cast, pick 1 friendly **Lumineth Realm-lords** unit wholly within 18" of the caster that is visible to them. You can heal up to D3 wounds allocated to that unit. In addition, do not take battleshock tests for that unit until your next hero phase.

5 **Burning Simoom:** *The caster incites a furious, blazing-hot wind to rush through the foe's ranks, searing their flesh and setting their lungs aflame.*

Burning Simoom has a casting value of 6. If successfully cast, pick 1 enemy unit within 12" of the caster that is visible to them and roll a number of dice equal to the number of models in that unit. For each 6, that unit suffers 1 mortal wound. If the casting roll was 10 or more, that unit suffers 1 mortal wound for each 5+ instead of each 6.

6 **Transporting Vortex:** *The caster calls upon a magnanimous whirlwind to sweep up their allies and carry them to safety.*

Transporting Vortex has a casting value of 8. If successfully cast, pick 1 friendly **Lumineth Realm-lords** unit wholly within 12" of the caster that is visible to them. Remove that unit from the battlefield and set it up again anywhere on the battlefield more than 9" from any enemy units. It cannot move in the next movement phase.

SHRINE LUMINOR

The Lumineth know how best to harness the free-floating metaliths that dot the Mortal Realms. They build shrines atop these wondrous islands, consecrating them to the aelementors they revere. When hovering over nexuses of power, the sanctified energies of the shrine purify the lands from the taint of Chaos.

When you choose a Lumineth Realm-lords army, you can include 1 **Shrine Luminor** terrain feature (pg 131).

After territories have been chosen but before armies are set up, you must set up the **Shrine Luminor** wholly within your territory, more than 1" from any other terrain features and more than 6" from where any objectives will be located at the start of the first battle round. If both players can set up any terrain features after territories have been chosen, they must roll off, and the winner chooses who sets up their terrain features first.

*I*llathusa gazed down as the Tangenati metalith moved at a stately pace across the tortured landscape, enjoying the warmth of the Parch's hot winds. For one who felt the cold, Aqshy's climes could be a blessing, and it was her vanguard's job to bless them in turn. The land below her floating shrine growled and spat, gobbets of molten rock leaving arcs of black smoke in the sky. Since the coming of the Age of Chaos, the muttering, growling disquiet of the lava-fields had become barking, coughing explosions of magma that precluded any decent civilisation being built there.

Already figures gathered in the distance at the Shrine Guardian's approach, no doubt joyful their salvation from disorder was close at hand. She spread her hands wide, recited the four meditations, and sent a calming pulse of energy across the lands. At first, nothing happened, but as Illathusa guided the Tangenati Shrine into place over a nexus of power, the volatile landscape began to calm. Red-hot lava turned to glowing stone, then salvageable land. In the wake of the shrine itself, green shoots were already pushing upward. Illathusa sighed in satisfaction. Then she saw the figures in the middle distance. They were charging, axes raised and tall red hair-crests waving as their fierce shouts of indignation carried on the hot thermals. 'Ah well,' sighed Illathusa as she prepared her mind for battle. 'One does not make a mosaic without shattering a few stones…'

The rune Minaith signifies Skill at Arms, Spirituality, and the Lost Way.

The rune Sendai is synonymous with Dedication, Sacrifice, and Resentment.

Quul translates as The Tree of Life, Regrowth, Decay, and the Oak of Ages Past.

Varinor, favoured in the Tyrionic nations, means Strength, Fire, and the Pride of Drakes.

Thanlui means Injustice, Necessity, and the Unbalanced Scale, but also the Shyish Nadir.

Ylvoir represents the Throne of Kings, but also Guardianship and Servitude.

Sethai, a subtle rune, means Flight, Wind, and the Cry in the Far Mountains.

Sevir, its aggressive equivalent, means Wind, Storm, and the Anger of the Realms.

• SCENERY WARSCROLL •

SHRINE LUMINOR

The most powerful Lumineth sages can tap into the power of a realmstone-rich metalith, and from there purify even the most corrupted battlefields of the energies that have ravaged it since the Age of Chaos. The aelves are lent a measure of geomantic power in the process, making their powers all the more formidable.

DESCRIPTION

A Shrine Luminor is a single terrain feature that can be garrisoned.

GARRISON: The garrison of a Shrine Luminor can be a single **LUMINETH REALM-LORDS HERO** model that is not a **MONSTER** and does not have a mount. The garrison is referred to as the terrain feature's 'Shrine Guardian' in the following rules.

SCENERY RULES

Cleansing Rituals: *A Shrine Luminor cleanses corruption from the lines of geomantic power that criss-cross the Mortal Realms.*

Once per turn, you can re-roll 1 casting, dispelling or unbinding roll for a friendly **LUMINETH REALM-LORDS HERO** that is within 12" of this terrain feature.

From the second battle round, in your hero phase, if this terrain feature has a Shrine Guardian, you can say that they will channel the shrine's power. If you do so, add 12" to the range of this ability.

Shrine Guardian: *Shrines Luminor are instrumental to the Lumineth's efforts in cleansing Chaos from the Mortal Realms, and the aelves will follow without question the commands of those who guard them.*

Once per turn, you can use a command ability with this terrain feature's Shrine Guardian without a command point being spent.

KEYWORDS	SCENERY, SHRINE LUMINOR

GREAT NATION OF ALUMNIA

The nation of Alumnia is typified by the mindset of the pioneer. Athletes, explorers and adventurers, they are only at peace when pushing into new territory. Taking command of the battlefield is second nature to their armies, whilst their heroes wield powers wrested from the most hostile places in the Mortal Realms.

Always pushing the limits of endurance, once the Alumnians set their minds upon something it will be done – even though many perish in the attempt. They prefer to attack from unexpected directions, and will push through the densest terrain and most unpredictable magical landscapes to ensure they have the advantage from the firing of the first arrow to the last killing blow.

Alumnians pride themselves on climbing the peaks of physical fitness. They are able to forced march for weeks on end or sprint fast enough to outdo the athletic champions of the other nations; when a Contest of Paragons is held, Alumnians usually fill the podiums. In battle they surge forwards with aggressive surety, wrong-footing the enemy with bursts of speed and agility, or – in the case of their most vaunted leaders – even vanishing from sight to appear in striking range of a choice foe. Those who have fought their way past dangers both mundane and metaphysical to approach the Realm's Edge, pushing themselves to the border of physicality and beyond, are said to possess uncanny powers, and that the intensity of their gaze can even burn those who would spurn Hysh's purest form of light.

ABILITIES

Claim the Field: *Alumnian warriors can read the battlefield at a glance, surging forwards to claim it in the name of the Realm-lords.*

After armies are set up but before the first battle round begins, up to 3 friendly **Alumnia Vanari** or **Alumnia Scinari** units can make a normal move but cannot run.

COMMAND TRAIT

An **Alumnia** general must have this command trait instead of one listed on pages 126-128 or in *Battletome: Lumineth Realm-lords*.

Burning Gaze: *Many Alumnians make pilgrimages to Hysh's Perimeter Inimical. Though few return from such a perilous journey, those who do are gifted with extraordinary powers; some can even sear a foe with a simple glance.*

At the start of the combat phase, you can pick 1 enemy unit within 3" of this general and visible to them, and roll a dice. On a 2+, that enemy unit suffers 1 mortal wound.

COMMAND ABILITY

Seize the Moment: *In battle, Alumnian warriors strike incredibly swiftly, launching themselves at an unsuspecting foe with an extraordinary burst of speed.*

You can use this command ability in your charge phase. If you do so, pick 1 friendly **Alumnia** unit that ran in that turn. That unit can charge in that charge phase.

ARTEFACT OF POWER

The first **Alumnia Hero** to receive an artefact of power must be given the Waystone.

Waystone: *This small sliver of dark rock hovers above the bearer's outstretched palm, leading them along hidden paths towards that which they desire.*

Once per battle in your movement phase, instead of making a normal move with the bearer, you can pick a point on the battlefield within 12" of them. If you do so, remove the bearer from the battlefield and set them up again within 1" of that point and more than 3" away from any enemy units.

GREAT NATION OF HELON

The many winds of Hysh form both muse and ally to the Helonites. Their landscape is forever gale-swept, and they take inspiration from the aelementors of that land, fighting with arrow as well as blade to ensure they form an ever-moving, ephemeral force all but impossible to catch.

The windswept reaches of Helon are for the most part wide-open spaces, the skies inviting and the gales that whip across them all too happy to bear the brave into the air. It has long been tradition for the Helonites to learn to fly upon the winds of their homelands, and as youths they compete as to who can do so with the most speed, dexterity and ingenuity. Just as Ymetrica is famous for its majestic mountain ranges, Helon is famed for its hovering, windswept metaliths; its landscape is replete with wondrous feats of erosion-carving and wind-sculpting, and the number of Hurakan temples that stand proud atop its floating shrines exceed those of any other nation. Scinari and Vanari alike practise the flowing, spinning martial forms that allow them to slip away from one foe and dart past to strike another, as unpredictable and changeable as a summer zephyr one moment, and as destructive as a winter storm the next. Despite their massed archers and abundant Hurakan devotees, is not always their way to engage at range; those who succeed in closing with a Helonite warhost will find themselves swiftly pincushioned. It is a point of pride to the marksmen of Helon that the closer the enemy gets, the more arrows will find him.

ABILITIES
Gale of Killing Shafts: *At close range, Helonite archers unleash a barrage of missiles that leaves enemies reeling.*

Add 1 to the Attacks characteristic of missile weapons used by **Helon** models that are within 3" of an enemy unit.

COMMAND TRAIT
A **Helon** general must have this command trait instead of one listed on pages 126-128 or in *Battletome: Lumineth Realm-lords.*

Skyrace Grand Champion: *This general is a celebrated champion of the contests of speed, dexterity and will at the Great Skyrace of Helon.*

Once per battle, you can re-roll 1 run roll, and 1 charge roll, and 1 casting roll for this general.

COMMAND ABILITY
Gone Like The Wind: *The competitive Helonites relish demonstrating their skill in close combat, but at a word from their commanders they will turn and swiftly move away, leaving foes bloodied and disordered in their wake.*

You can use this command ability at the end of the combat phase. If you do so, pick 1 friendly **Helon** unit that fought in that phase and is wholly within 12" of a friendly **Helon Hero**. That unit can make a normal move but cannot run (it can retreat).

ARTEFACT OF POWER
The first **Helon Hero** to receive an artefact of power must be given Metalith Dust.

Metalith Dust: *Metalith dust is gathered from the floating islands of Helon. If thrown at a foe, it renders them weightless and incapable of landing solid blows for a short while.*

Once per battle, at the start of the combat phase, you can pick 1 enemy unit within 3" of the bearer. If you do so, subtract 1 from hit rolls and wound rolls for attacks made by that unit until the end of that phase.

BATTLEPLAN
THE SCOURING WIND

As part of Teclis' masterplan, the Lumineth Realm-lords have established a number of beachheads around isolated Realmgates across all the Mortal Realms. Hurakan raiding parties are sent out from these enclaves, striking at the enemies of Order and scouring all signs of their presence from landscape.

THE ARMIES

Each player picks an army as described in the core rules. One player is the Lumineth Realm-lords player and their opponent is the Upstart.

The Lumineth Realm-lords player must use a Lumineth Realm-lords army consisting of 5 units from the following list:

- 1 Hurakan Windmage.

- 0-1 Sevireth, Lord of the Seventh Wind,
  or 0-1 Alarith Spirit of the Mountain,
  or 0-1 Ellania and Ellathor.

- 2-4 Hurakan Windchargers units, each of up to 5 models.

- 0-1 Scinari Loreseeker,
  or 0-1 Vanari Dawnriders unit of up to 5 models,
  or 0-1 Vanari Auralan Sentinels unit of up to 10 models,
  or 0-1 Vanari Auralan Wardens unit of up to 10 models,
  or 0-1 Vanari Bladelords unit of up to 5 models.

The Upstart's army has 5 units, each of which must conform to a unit type from the following list:

- Horde unit: A unit of up to 20 models, each with a Wounds characteristic of 1 and a Save characteristic of 6+ or '-'.

- Regular unit: A unit of up to 10 models, each with a Wounds characteristic of 1 and a Save characteristic of 3+, 4+ or 5+.

- Elite unit: A unit of up to 5 models, each with a Wounds characteristic of 2 or 3.

- Guard unit: A unit of up to 3 models, each with a Wounds characteristic of 4 or 5.

- Linebreaker unit: A unit of 1 model with a Wounds characteristic of 6 to 9 that is not a **Hero**.

- Champion: A **Hero** that is not a **Monster**.

OBJECTIVES

Set up 5 objectives as shown on the map.

SET-UP

The Upstart player sets up 5 units from their army. Each unit must be set up wholly within 6" of a different objective.

All units in the Lumineth Realm-lords army start the battle in reserve and will arrive as described later (see The Scouring Wind).

FIRST TURN

The Lumineth Realm-lords player takes the first turn in the first battle round.

THE WINDS ARRIVE

With the roar of rushing winds the Hurakan cleansing force arrives, ready to unleash retribution on the upstart intruders that have sullied the Mortal Realms.

At the start of their first movement phase, the Lumineth Realm-lords

UPSTART'S TERRITORY

134

player must pick 1 point anywhere on the edge of the battlefield. During that movement phase, all of the Lumineth Realm-lords units must enter the battlefield by making a normal move (they can run). Use the point on the edge of the battlefield as the starting point of the move for each of the reserve units.

THE SCOURING WIND
The Hurakan raiders race across the battlefield, leaving only wind-scoured ruins in their wake.

At the end of each of their turns, the Lumineth Realm-lords player can scour any objectives in enemy territory that they control. An objective that has been scoured is removed from play.

BATTLE LENGTH
The battle lasts for 5 battle rounds.

GLORIOUS VICTORY
At the end of the battle, look up the number of objectives that have been scoured to determine the result of the battle:

Scoured Objectives	Result
0-1	Upstart **major victory**
2	Upstart **minor victory**
3	**Draw**
4	Lumineth Realm-lords **minor victory**
5	Lumineth Realm-lords **major victory**

PATH TO GLORY

Path to Glory campaigns centre around collecting and fighting a series of battles in the Mortal Realms. Players start off with a small warband. Over the course of several battles, each warband will gather more followers to join them in their quest for glory and renown.

In order to take part in a Path to Glory campaign, you will need two or more players. Each player will need a **Hero** to be their champion and must then create a warband to follow their champion into battle.

The players fight battles against each other using the warbands they have created. The results of these battles will gain their warbands glory. After battle, warbands may swell in numbers as more warriors flock to their banner, or existing troops may become more powerful.

After gaining sufficient glory or growing your warband enough to dominate all others through sheer weight of numbers, you will be granted a final test. Succeed, and you will be crowned the victor of the campaign, your glory affirmed for all time.

CREATING A WARBAND
In a Path to Glory game, you do not select your army in the normal manner. Instead, you create a warband that consists of a mighty champion, battling to earn the favour of the gods, and their followers. The details and progress of each warband need to be recorded on a warband roster, which you can download for free from games-workshop.com.

To create a warband, simply follow these steps and record the results on your warband roster:

1. First, pick a faction for your warband. Each faction has its own set of warband tables that are used to generate the units in the warband and the rewards they can receive for fighting battles. The warband tables included in this battletome let you collect a Lumineth Realm-lords warband, but other *Warhammer Age of Sigmar* publications include warband tables to let you collect warbands from other factions.

2. Next, choose your warband's champion by selecting one of the options from your faction's champion table. Give your champion a suitably grand name and write this down on your warband roster.

3. Having picked your champion, the next step is to make follower rolls to generate your starting followers. The champion you chose in step 2 will determine how many follower rolls you have. To make a follower roll, pick a column from one of the followers tables and then roll a dice. If you prefer, instead of rolling a dice, you can pick the result from the followers table (this still uses up the roll).

   Sometimes a table will require you to expend two or more rolls, or one roll and a number of Glory Points (see Gaining Glory), in order to use it. Note that the option to expend Glory Points can only be used when you add new followers to your army after a battle (see Rewards of Battle). In either case, in order to generate a follower unit from the table, you must have enough rolls and/or Glory Points to meet the requirements, and you can then either roll once on the table or pick one result from the table of your choice. If you expend Glory Points, you must reduce your Glory Points total by the amount shown on the table.

   Followers are organised into units. The followers table tells you how many models the unit has. Follower units cannot include additional models, but they can otherwise take any options allowed by their warscroll. Record all of the information about your followers on your warband roster.

4. You can use 1 follower roll to allow your champion to start the campaign with a Champion's

Reward or to allow 1 of your follower units to start the campaign with a Follower's Reward (see Rewards of Battle).

5. Finally, give your warband a name, one that will inspire respect and dread in your rivals. Your warband is now complete and you can fight your first battle. Good luck!

TO WAR!
Having created a warband, you can now fight battles with it against other warbands taking part in the campaign. You can fight battles as and when you wish, and you can use any of the battleplans available for Warhammer Age of Sigmar. The units you use for a game must be those on your roster.

When you use a Lumineth Realm-lords warband in a Path to Glory game, you can use any of the battle traits from pages 125-128 except for the Lumineth Great Nations battle trait. You cannot use any other Lumineth Realm-lords allegiance abilities.

Any casualties suffered by a warband are assumed to have been replaced in time for its next battle. If your champion is slain in a battle, it is assumed that they were merely injured; they are back to full strength for your next game, thirsty for vengeance!

GAINING GLORY
All of the players in the campaign are vying for glory. The amount of glory they have received is represented by the Glory Points that the warband has accumulated. As a warband's glory increases, it will also attract additional followers, and a warband's champion may be granted rewards.

Warbands receive Glory Points after a battle is complete. If the warband drew or lost the battle, it receives 1

Glory Point. If it won the battle, it receives D3 Glory Points (re-roll a result of 1 if it won a **major victory**).

Add the Glory Points you scored to the total recorded on your roster. Once you have won 10 Glory Points, you will have a chance to win the campaign (see Eternal Glory).

REWARDS OF BATTLE

After each battle, you can take one of the three following options. Alternatively, roll a D3 to determine which option to take.

D3	Option
1	**Additional Followers:** *More loyal followers flock to your banner.*

You receive 1 follower roll that can be used to select a new unit from a followers table and add it to your warband roster. See step 3 of Creating a Warband for details of how to use the followers table to add a unit to your army. Once 5 new units have joined your warband, you will have a chance to win the campaign (see Eternal Glory).

2	**Champion's Reward:** *Your champion's prowess grows.*

Roll on your champion rewards table for your warband and note the result on your warband roster. Your champion can only receive 1 Champion's Reward – if they already have a Champion's Reward, you must take a Follower's Reward instead.

3	**Follower's Reward:** *Your warriors become renowned for mighty deeds.*

Pick 1 unit of followers and then roll on the followers rewards table for your warband. Note the result on your warband roster. A unit can only receive 1 Follower's Reward. If all of your follower units have a Follower's Reward, you must take Additional Followers instead.

ETERNAL GLORY

There are two ways to win a Path to Glory campaign: by Blood or by Might. To win by Blood, your warband must first have 10 Glory Points. To win by Might, your warband must have at least 5 additional units of followers. In either case, you must then fight and win one more battle to win the campaign. If the next battle you fight is tied or lost, you do not receive any Glory Points – just keep on fighting battles until you win the campaign... or another player wins first!

You can shorten or lengthen a campaign by lowering or raising the number of Glory Points needed to win by Blood or the number of extra units that must join a warband to win by Might. For example, for a shorter campaign, you could say that a warband only needs 5 Glory Points before the final fight, or for a longer one, you could say that 15 are needed.

LUMINETH REALM-LORDS WARBAND TABLES

Use the following tables to determine the champion that leads your warband, the followers that make up the units that fight at their side, and the rewards they receive after battle.

CHAMPION TABLE

Champion	Follower Rolls
Hurakan Windmage	5
Scinari Calligrave	5
Vanari Lord Regent	4
Alarith Stonemage	4
Scinari Cathallar	4

RETINUE FOLLOWERS TABLE

D6	Followers
1-2	10 Vanari Auralan Wardens
3-4	5 Vanari Auralan Sentinels or 5 Vanari Dawnriders
5	5 Vanari Bladelords or 1 Vanari Starshard Ballista
6	5 Alarith Stoneguard or 5 Hurakan Windchargers

LUMINETH AVATAR FOLLOWERS TABLE
(uses 4 rolls, or 1 roll and 3 Glory Points)

D6	Followers
1-3	Alarith Spirit of the Mountain
4-6	Hurakan Spirit of the Wind

HERO FOLLOWERS TABLE

D6	Followers
1	Vanari Bannerblade
2	Scinari Calligrave
3	Hurakan Windmage
4	Alarith Stonemage
5-6	Scinari Cathallar

RETINUE FOLLOWERS REWARDS TABLE

D6   Reward

1   Gleaming Brightness: *The sheer concentration of aetherquartz that these warriors have fashioned into their raiment of war flaunts their wealth for all to see.*

This unit starts the battle with 2 aetherquartz reserves instead of 1.

2   Lambent Mystics: *These followers are exceptionally gifted in the arcane arts. It is said that the power of magic runs through their veins.*

Add 1 to the first casting, dispelling or unbinding roll you make for this unit in each hero phase.

3   Soul-bond: *These followers are soul-bonded twins, none of whom will desert their siblings either in life or in death.*

Add 2 to the Bravery characteristic of this unit.

4   Shield of Light: *When these warriors stand together, they radiate a dazzling light that protects them from their foes.*

You can re-roll save rolls of 1 for attacks that target this unit while this unit has 5 or more models.

5   Shafts of Light: *These followers radiate blinding shafts of light that befuddle and disorientate, leaving the foe horribly vulnerable to attack.*

You can re-roll hit rolls of 1 for attacks made with melee weapons by this unit while this unit has 5 or more models.

6   Blessing of Teclis: *Teclis has blessed this unit with a shield of magical energy for its protection.*

Roll a dice each time you allocate a wound or mortal wound to this unit. On a 6, that wound or mortal wound is negated.

CHAMPION AND HERO FOLLOWERS REWARDS TABLE

(Lumineth Avatar followers cannot receive rewards)

2D6   Reward

2   Twin Commanders: *This champion has a soul-bonded twin. They act in unison as if one mind were in two bodies.*

Pick 1 other friendly model in your warband to be this model's twin. In your hero phase, if both of these models are on the battlefield, you receive 1 extra command point.

3   Goading Arrogance: *This champion uses an appearance of arrogance and superiority as a feint, goading the enemy into foolhardy attacks.*

At the start of the combat phase, you can pick 1 enemy **Hero** within 3" of this model. That enemy **Hero** can only target this model in that phase. In addition, you can add 1 to hit rolls for attacks that target that enemy **Hero** in that phase.

4   Swordmaster: *This champion has studied the art of the blade for centuries.*

You can re-roll hit rolls for attacks made with melee weapons by this model.

5   Enduring: *This champion's stamina is legendary.*

Add 2 to this model's Wounds characteristic.

6   Warmaster: *This champion has mastered advanced strategies and tactics of battle.*

If this model is part of your army and on the battlefield at the start of your hero phase, roll a dice. On a 4+, you receive 1 extra command point.

7   Majestic: *Few can look upon this champion and not be awed by their luminous majesty.*

Add 1 to the Bravery characteristic of friendly **Lumineth Realm-lords** units while they are wholly within 12" of this model. In addition, subtract 1 from the Bravery characteristic of enemy units they are within 18" of this model.

8   Loremaster: *Few can rival this champion's knowledge of aelven magic.*

This model knows 1 extra spell from the Lore of Hysh (see *Battletome: Lumineth Realm-lords*)

9   Mystic: *This champion is exceptionally gifted in the arcane arts. It is said that the power of magic runs through their veins.*

Add 1 to casting, dispelling and unbinding rolls for this model.

10   Mighty: *The blows made by this champion land with shattering might.*

Add 1 to wound rolls for attacks made with melee weapons by this model.

11   Thirst for Knowledge: *This champion is endlessly fascinated by any form of magic, studying it intently in order to unravel its secrets.*

Add 1 to unbinding rolls for this model if the spell they are attempting to unbind has been successfully cast and not unbound at least once before in the battle. Add 2 to unbinding rolls for this model instead of 1 if the spell they are attempting to unbind has been successfully cast and not unbound at least 3 times before in the battle.

12   Artefact of Power: *An ancient artefact of power has come into this champion's possession.*

Randomly generate 1 artefact of power for this model from the appropriate Artefacts of Power table (pg 126-128).

WARSCROLLS

This section includes Lumineth Realm-lords warscrolls and warscroll battalions. Updated March 2021; the warscrolls printed here take precedence over any warscrolls with an earlier publication date or no publication date.

WARSCROLL BATTALION
LUMINETH BATTLEHOST

It is rare that the Lumineth gather for war in great numbers, but when they field a host that brings together the wisdom of the Scinari, the might of the Vanari, and the spiritual strength of the aelementiri, they are almost unstoppable. The air shimmers and gleams around the shining companies as they advance, the leaders of each element sharing their expertise so they may better bring the light of Hyshian conquest to the barbaric and the cruel.

ORGANISATION

- 1 Vanari Lord Regent
- 1 Vanari Bannerblade
- 0-3 **Scinari Heroes**
- 0-1 Alarith Temple
- 0-1 Hurakan Temple
- 1-2 Auralan Legions
- 1-2 Dawnrider Lance
- 1 Bladelord Host
- 1 Starshard Battery

ABILITIES

Extraordinary Discipline: *The commanders of this elite formation, and the warriors they lead, are some of the most skilful in all of the Mortal Realms.*

If this battalion is part of your army, at the start of your hero phase, roll a dice for each **Hero** from this battalion that is on the battlefield. For each 6, you receive 1 extra command point.

WARSCROLL BATTALION
HURAKAN TEMPLE

ORGANISATION

- Sevireth, Lord of the Seventh Wind or 1 Hurakan Spirit of the Wind
- 1 Hurakan Windmage
- 1-3 units of Hurakan Windchargers

ABILITIES

Whirling Tornadoes: *When the warriors of the Hurakan gather together in battle, the combined powers of their swirling aelementor allies allow them to run rings around their enemies with startling swiftness.*

If a unit from this battalion is wholly within 12" of a **Hero** from the same battalion at the start of the combat phase, the models in that unit count as having made a charge move in the same turn.

Designer's Note: *This means that, when they pile in, these models can fly and move an extra 3" as described in the Move Like the Wind battle trait (pg 128) without actually having to have made a charge move in the same turn.*

WARSCROLL BATTALION
STARSHARD BATTERY

ORGANISATION

- 1 Scinari Calligrave
- 3-5 units of Vanari Starshards

ABILITIES

Ward Barrier: *Under the shrewd guidance of a Scinari Calligrave, the crews of a Starshard Battery deploy their aetherquartz lanterns so that they create overlapping fields of protective energy.*

If a **Starshard Ballistas** unit from this battalion is within 3" of another **Starshard Ballistas** unit from the same battalion, replace its Warding Lanterns ability with: 'Roll a dice each time you allocate a wound or mortal wound to this unit if it has not made a move in the same turn. On a 5+, that wound or mortal wound is negated. In addition, add 1 to the Attacks characteristic of this unit's Starshard Bolts if it has not made a move in the same turn.'

WARSCROLL BATTALION
BLADELORD HOST

ORGANISATION

- 1 **Vanari** or **Scinari Hero**
- 2-3 units of Vanari Bladelords

ABILITIES

Calculated Response: *Analysing potential weaknesses of the enemy even as they charge towards the Lumineth's lines, the warriors in a Bladelord Host swiftly adopt a formation that is calculated to use their opponents' momentum against them.*

You can re-roll hit rolls of 1 for attacks made with melee weapons by units from this battalion that target an enemy unit that has made a charge move in the same turn.

LYRIOR UTHRALLE
WARDEN OF YMETRICA

MOVE		
16"		
WOUNDS 6	✕	SAVE 3+
9		
BRAVERY		

Lyrior Uthralle fights with the confidence of a demigod, darting through the fray on his lightcourser steed, Farael. Though deeply scarred by the loss of his family to a tribe of orruks, he is a true statesman, and knows well his first duty is to defeat Chaos.

MISSILE WEAPONS	Range	Attacks	To Hit	To Wound	Rend	Damage
Daemonbane	18"	1	2+	2+	-2	D3
MELEE WEAPONS	Range	Attacks	To Hit	To Wound	Rend	Damage
Daemonbane	3"	1	2+	2+	-2	D3
Regent's Sword	1"	5	2+	3+	-1	1
Horns and Claws	1"	4	3+	4+	-	1

DESCRIPTION

Lyrior Uthralle is a named character that is a single model. He is armed with Daemonbane and a Regent's Sword.

MOUNT: Farael attacks with his Horns and Claws.

ABILITIES

Daemonbane: *Lyrior's arcane lance can send out a beam of exorcising light that inflicts terrible damage, especially on the daemonic minions of the Chaos Gods.*

The damage inflicted by a successful attack made with Daemonbane is 3 instead of D3 if the target has the **CHAOS** and **DAEMON** keywords.

Purest Aetherquartz: *Every Lord Regent carries a reserve of the finest aetherquartz, which burns with the dazzling brilliance of Hysh.*

Subtract 1 from hit rolls for attacks that target this model, and add 1 to the casting roll when it attempts to cast Greater Power of Hysh. If this model is part of a Lumineth Realm-lords army and uses its last aetherquartz reserve, this ability cannot be used by this model for the rest of the battle.

Sunmetal Weapons: *The blades carried by Vanari Lord Regents are forged from sunmetal, which can burn a victim from the inside out.*

If the unmodified hit roll for an attack made with a Regent's Sword is 6, that attack inflicts 1 mortal wound on the target and the attack sequence ends (do not make a wound or save roll).

Voice of Tyrion: *Lyrior is part of Tyrion's inner circle, and he speaks with the authority of the god himself in matters military.*

If this model is part of your army and on the battlefield at the start of your hero phase, and **TECLIS** is not part of your army, roll a dice. On a 2+, you receive 1 command point.

MAGIC

This model is a **WIZARD**. It can attempt to cast 1 spell in your hero phase and attempt to unbind 1 spell in the enemy hero phase. It knows the Greater Power of Hysh spell.

Greater Power of Hysh: *Lumineth wizards can use their arcane arts to empower sunmetal, making it burn with an even greater intensity.*

Greater Power of Hysh has a casting value of 7. If successfully cast, pick up to D3 friendly **LUMINETH REALM-LORDS** units with the Sunmetal Weapons ability that are wholly within 18" of the caster and visible to them. Until your next hero phase, the Sunmetal Weapons ability of those units causes mortal wounds to be inflicted on an unmodified hit roll of 5+ instead of 6.

KEYWORDS	ORDER, AELF, LUMINETH REALM-LORDS, VANARI, YMETRICA, HERO, WIZARD, LORD REGENT, LYRIOR UTHRALLE

VANARI LORD REGENT

MOVE	14"	
WOUNDS	6	SAVE 3+
	8	
BRAVERY		

Each Lord Regent carries high authority within the Vanari military, for they are representatives of Tyrion himself. These august warriors glow with the highly charged aetherquartz they wear, inspiring those around them through word as well as deed.

MELEE WEAPONS	Range	Attacks	To Hit	To Wound	Rend	Damage
Regent's Sword	1"	5	2+	3+	-1	1
Horns and Claws	1"	3	3+	4+	-	1

DESCRIPTION

A Vanari Lord Regent is a single model armed with a Regent's Sword.

MOUNT: This model's Lightcourser attacks with its Horns and Claws.

ABILITIES

Purest Aetherquartz: *Every Lord Regent carries a reserve of the finest aetherquartz, which burns with the dazzling brilliance of Hysh.*

Subtract 1 from hit rolls for attacks that target this model, and add 1 to the casting roll when it attempts to cast Greater Power of Hysh. If this model is part of a Lumineth Realm-lords army and uses its last aetherquartz reserve, this ability cannot be used by this model for the rest of the battle.

Sunmetal Weapons: *The blades carried by Vanari Lord Regents are forged from sunmetal, which can burn a victim from the inside out.*

If the unmodified hit roll for an attack made with a Regent's Sword is 6, that attack inflicts 1 mortal wound on the target and the attack sequence ends (do not make a wound or save roll).

MAGIC

This model is a **WIZARD**. It can attempt to cast 1 spell in your hero phase and attempt to unbind 1 spell in the enemy hero phase. It knows the Greater Power of Hysh spell.

Greater Power of Hysh: *Lumineth wizards can use their arcane arts to empower sunmetal, making it burn with an even greater intensity.*

Greater Power of Hysh has a casting value of 7. If successfully cast, pick up to D3 friendly **LUMINETH REALM-LORDS** units with the Sunmetal Weapons ability that are wholly within 18" of the caster and visible to them. Until your next hero phase, the Sunmetal Weapons ability of those units causes mortal wounds to be inflicted on an unmodified hit roll of 5+ instead of 6.

KEYWORDS	ORDER, AELF, LUMINETH REALM-LORDS, VANARI, HERO, WIZARD, LORD REGENT

VANARI BANNERBLADE

MOVE	6"	
WOUNDS	5	SAVE 3+
	8	
BRAVERY		

The central point of many a Vanari battleline, each Bannerblade is a locus of surety in the maelstrom of battle. The World Banners they bear are priceless artefacts, for they can unleash the power of a Hyshian dawn to blind, melt and even kill.

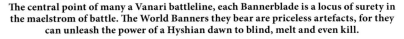

MELEE WEAPONS	Range	Attacks	To Hit	To Wound	Rend	Damage
Bannerblade's Sword	1"	4	2+	3+	-1	1

DESCRIPTION

A Vanari Bannerblade is a single model armed with a Bannerblade's Sword.

ABILITIES

World Banner: *This mighty standard is adorned with symbols of great importance to the Lumineth. In extremis, it can be used to unleash a blast of Hyshian energy to smite enemies.*

Add 1 to the Bravery characteristic of friendly **LUMINETH REALM-LORDS** units that are wholly within 18" of any friendly **BANNERBLADES**. Add 3 instead of 1 if any of those **BANNERBLADES** is within 3" of any enemy units.

In addition, once per battle at the start of any phase, you can say that this model will draw on the power of its World Banner. If you do so, roll a dice for each enemy unit within 18" of this model. If the roll is equal to or less than the number of the current battle round, that unit suffers D3 mortal wounds, and subtract 1 from hit rolls for that unit until the end of that phase.

Sunmetal Weapons: *The swords carried by Vanari Bannerblades are forged from sunmetal, which can burn a victim from the inside out.*

If the unmodified hit roll for an attack made with a Bannerblade's Sword is 6, that attack inflicts 1 mortal wound on the target and the attack sequence ends (do not make a wound or save roll).

KEYWORDS	ORDER, AELF, LUMINETH REALM-LORDS, VANARI, HERO, TOTEM, BANNERBLADE

VANARI STARSHARD BALLISTAS

MOVE 6"
WOUNDS 5
SAVE 5+
BRAVERY 6

No normal ballistas, Vanari Starshards fire twin bolts of such fine craftsmanship they can punch through Chaos warplate. At need, their crews can load bolts that blind as well as maim, and they employ warding lanterns that likewise steal the enemy's sight.

MISSILE WEAPONS	Range	Attacks	To Hit	To Wound	Rend	Damage
Starshard Bolts	30"	2	3+	3+	-2	D3
MELEE WEAPONS	Range	Attacks	To Hit	To Wound	Rend	Damage
Arming Swords	1"	2	3+	4+	-	1

DESCRIPTION
A unit of Vanari Starshard Ballistas has any number of models, each armed with Starshard Bolts and Arming Swords.

ABILITIES
Blinding Bolts: *A Starshard can be loaded with specialised bolts that explode with blinding light when they strike a target.*

Once per battle, when you pick this unit to shoot, you can say that it will fire its blinding bolts. If you do so, units that are hit by an attack made by this unit in that phase are dazzled until the end of the turn. Subtract 1 from hit rolls for a unit that is dazzled. A unit cannot be dazzled more than once per turn.

Messenger Hawk: *Every Starshard ballista is accompanied by a messenger hawk, which is used by the leaders of the army to direct the crew's fire towards the most important targets.*

At the start of your shooting phase, you can pick 1 enemy unit within 24" of a friendly **Realm-lords Hero** and pick 1 friendly **Starshard Ballistas** unit within 24" of that **Hero**. If you do so, add 1 to hit rolls for attacks made by that **Starshard Ballistas** unit that target that enemy unit until the end of the phase.

Warding Lanterns: *The crew of a Starshard ballista carry deployable aetherquartz lanterns that aid accuracy and dazzle attackers.*

Roll a dice each time you allocate a wound or mortal wound to this unit if it has not made a move in the same turn. On a 6, that wound or mortal wound is negated. In addition, add 1 to the Attacks characteristic of this unit's Starshard Bolts if it has not made a move in the same turn.

KEYWORDS	ORDER, AELF, LUMINETH REALM-LORDS, VANARI, STARSHARD BALLISTAS

VANARI BLADELORDS

MOVE 6"
WOUNDS 2
SAVE 4+
BRAVERY 7

Bladelords are preternaturally talented in the art of the sword. Though of the Vanari, they are seconded to the Scinari, forming bodyguards for the Lumineth's mages. In return they enjoy potent magical protection that sees them safe to the front line.

MELEE WEAPONS	Range	Attacks	To Hit	To Wound	Rend	Damage
Sunmetal Greatblade: Perfect Strike	2"	1	See below	2+	-2	1
Sunmetal Greatblade: Flurry of Blows	2"	See below	3+	3+	-	1
Sunmetal Dual Blades	1"	3	2+	3+	-1	1

DESCRIPTION
A unit of Vanari Bladelords has any number of models, each armed with a Sunmetal Greatblade.

BLADELORD SENESCHAL: 1 model in this unit can be a Bladelord Seneschal. That model is armed with a Sunmetal Greatblade or Sunmetal Dual Blades. Add 1 to the Attacks characteristic a Bladelord Seneschal's Sunmetal Greatblade.

ABILITIES
Guardians: *Bladelords most commonly fight alongside Scinari, protecting them from harm.*

Roll a dice before you allocate a wound or mortal wound to a friendly **Scinari** model within 3" of any friendly units with this ability. On a 2+, you must allocate that wound or mortal wound to a friendly unit with this ability within 3" of that model, instead of to that model.

Swordmasters: *Vanari Bladelords adopt different fighting styles depending upon the nature of their opponents.*

Before fighting with this unit, choose either the Perfect Strike or Flurry of Blows Sunmetal Greatblade weapon characteristics. All of the models in the unit armed with Sunmetal

Greatblades must use those characteristics when they attack. A Perfect Strike always hits (do not make a hit roll). A Flurry of Blows has an Attacks characteristic equal to the number of enemy models within 2" of the attacking model.

Vanashimor Banners: *The banners worn by Vanari Bladelords, woven for them by the Scinari they protect, are proof against hostile magics.*

Each time this unit is affected by a spell or endless spell, you can roll a dice. If you do so, on a 4+, ignore the effects of that spell or endless spell on this unit.

KEYWORDS	ORDER, AELF, LUMINETH REALM-LORDS, VANARI, BLADELORDS

SCINARI CALLIGRAVE

A Calligrave is an arcane specialist who changes reality with the stroke of a brush.
Those runes he paints upon his enchanted parchments emblazon the battlefield a
moment later, his spells writ large to burn the foe – or even erase them from existence.

MELEE WEAPONS	Range	Attacks	To Hit	To Wound	Rend	Damage
Calligrave Blade	3"	D3	3+	3+	-1	D3

MOVE 6"
WOUNDS 5
SAVE 5+
BRAVERY 7

DESCRIPTION

A Scinari Calligrave is a single model armed with a Calligrave Blade.

ABILITIES

Realmscribe: *With intense concentration, the Calligrave inscribes a rune whose vast, blazing parallel simultaneously appears upon the battlefield.*

Once per battle, in your hero phase, instead of attempting to cast any spells with 1 friendly model with this ability, you can roll a dice. Add the number of the current battle round to the roll. On a 5+, pick a point anywhere on the battlefield. For the rest of the battle, do not take battleshock tests for friendly **LUMINETH REALM-LORDS** units that are wholly within 9" of that point, and add 1 to casting, dispelling and unbinding rolls for friendly **LUMINETH REALM-LORDS WIZARDS** that are within 9" of that point.

MAGIC

This model is a **WIZARD**. It can attempt to cast 1 spell in your hero phase and attempt to unbind 1 spell in the enemy hero phase. It knows the Arcane Bolt, Mystic Shield and Erasure spells.

Erasure: *With a deft flourish, the Calligrave swiftly scribes a rune that opens gaping wounds in the flesh of a foe, or concentrates on creating a more intricate symbol in preparation to wipe the target from existence entirely.*

Erasure has a casting value of 7. If successfully cast, pick 1 enemy **HERO** within 24" of the caster. You can either inflict D3 wounds on that **HERO** or mark them for erasure. However, if that **HERO** is already marked for erasure, then instead they suffer D6 mortal wounds and they are no longer marked for erasure.

KEYWORDS	ORDER, AELF, LUMINETH REALM-LORDS, SCINARI, HERO, WIZARD, CALLIGRAVE

SCINARI LORESEEKER

Loreseekers strike a perfect balance between the Tyrionic and the Teclian disciplines,
and they find great power in that harmony. They know the secrets of the realms: where
to look for esoteric artefacts, and how best to make use of them when they are found.

MOVE 6"
WOUNDS 6
SAVE 4+
BRAVERY 8

MISSILE WEAPONS	Range	Attacks	To Hit	To Wound	Rend	Damage
Eclipsian Staff	12"	2	3+	3+	-2	D3
MELEE WEAPONS	Range	Attacks	To Hit	To Wound	Rend	Damage
Loreseeker Blade	1"	4	2+	3+	-1	D3

DESCRIPTION

A Scinari Loreseeker is a single model armed with an Eclipsian Staff and Loreseeker Blade.

ABILITIES

Loreseeker: *Scinari Loreseekers bring the enemy's secrets to light and turn them to the advantage of the Lumineth.*

If an enemy model that bears an artefact of power is slain within 3" of any friendly models with this ability, you receive 1 command point.

Lone Agent: *Scinari Loreseekers employ their skills as independent operatives to great effect upon the field of battle.*

You can add 1 to save rolls for attacks that target this model if it is more than 9" from any friendly models.

In addition, instead of setting up this model on the battlefield, you can place it to one side and say that it is set up as a Lone Agent reserve unit. If you do so, at the start of the first battle round, before determining who has the first turn, you must set up this model on the battlefield anywhere that is more than 3" from any enemy units and not in your territory. If you set up this model within 6" of an objective that has no enemy units within 6" of it, you gain control of that objective, and your opponent cannot gain control of it while this model is within 6" of it.

MAGIC

This model is a **WIZARD**. It can attempt to cast 1 spell in your hero phase and attempt to unbind 1 spell in the enemy hero phase. It knows the Arcane Bolt and Mystic Shield spells.

KEYWORDS	ORDER, AELF, LUMINETH REALM-LORDS, SCINARI, HERO, WIZARD, LORESEEKER

ELLANIA AND ELLATHOR
ECLIPSIAN WARSAGES

MOVE 6"
WOUNDS 8
SAVE 3+
BRAVERY 8

The twins Ellania and Ellathor are prodigies, lacking in experience, but making up for it with unalloyed excellence. Fate smiles upon them, for their patrons are gods – Teclis has gifted the mage Ellania with his tutelage, just as Tyrion favours Ellathor.

MELEE WEAPONS	Range	Attacks	To Hit	To Wound	Rend	Damage
Altairi	1"	4	2+	3+	-2	See below
Dianaer	1"	2	3+	3+	-1	D3
Moonbright Talons	1"	2	3+	3+	-1	1

DESCRIPTION

Ellania and Ellathor are named characters that are a single model. They are armed with the blade Altairi and the staff Dianaer.

COMPANION: Ellania and Ellathor are accompanied by the lune-owl Atheane, who attacks with her Moonbright Talons.

ABILITIES

Aspect of Celennar: *Ellania enjoys the protection of Celennar and is accompanied by an owl familiar that grants her a measure of the moon-spirit's arcane knowledge and insight.*

Add 1 to casting, dispelling and unbinding rolls for this model.

Realm Wanderers: *Ellania and Ellathor travel the Mortal Realms searching for knowledge, helping any who fight for Order along the way.*

This model can be included as an ally in armies that have an **ORDER** general. In addition, if this model is within 3" of your general at the start of your hero phase, roll a dice. On a 4+, you receive 1 extra command point. However, this model can never be a general.

Altairi: *Tyrion has gifted Ellathor with an enchanted blade of awesome power that blazes with increasing intensity from the moment it is unsheathed in battle.*

The Damage characteristic of Altairi is equal to the number of the current battle round.

In addition, once per battle in your shooting phase, you can declare that Ellathor will unleash a blazing sunbolt. If you do so, pick 1 point on the battlefield within 12" of this model that is visible to it and draw an imaginary straight line 1mm wide between that point and the closest point on this model's base. Roll a dice for each unit that has any models passed across by this line. On a 2+, that unit suffers a number of mortal wounds equal to the number of the current battle round.

Sudden Translocation: *Should Ellathor use Altairi for too long, he will start to be overwhelmed by its arcane power, and Ellania will be forced to transport him away from the battle lest he be transformed into a creature of blazing fury.*

At the end of the combat phase, roll a dice if this model fought in that phase. If the roll is less than the number of the current battle round or less than the number of wounds allocated to this model, heal up to D6 wounds allocated to this model then remove it from the battlefield. Then, set up this model anywhere on the battlefield that is more than 12" from any enemy models. If this is impossible, this model is removed from play but does not count as having been slain.

MAGIC

This model is a **WIZARD**. It can attempt to cast 2 spells in your hero phase and attempt to unbind 2 spells in the enemy hero phase. It knows the Arcane Bolt, Mystic Shield and Salvation of Hysh spells.

Salvation of Hysh: *A veil of magical energy like a shimmering aurora descends upon the caster, protecting them from harm.*

Salvation of Hysh has a casting value of 6. If successfully cast, until your next hero phase, roll a dice each time a wound or mortal wound is allocated to the caster. On a 5+, that wound or mortal wound is negated.

KEYWORDS	ORDER, AELF, LUMINETH REALM-LORDS, SCINARI, VANARI, YMETRICA, HERO, WIZARD, ELLANIA AND ELLATHOR

HURAKAN WINDMAGE

	MOVE	
WOUNDS	16"	SAVE
5		5+
	7	
	BRAVERY	

Such is the mastery of the Windmages that they are carried at all times upon the winds they call their allies. They coax the aelementors to carry their fellow Hurakan into the air whilst visiting the gale-force wrath of Hyshian tempests upon their enemies.

MELEE WEAPONS	Range	Attacks	To Hit	To Wound	Rend	Damage
Aspiragillum	3"	2	3+	3+	-1	D3

DESCRIPTION

A Hurakan Windmage is a single model armed with an Aspiragillum.

FLY: This model can fly.

ABILITIES

Fan of Redirection: *The fan carried by a Windmage can be used to brush aside enemy missiles, redirecting them into the ground or even nearby foes.*

Add 1 to save rolls for attacks made with missile weapons that target this model. In addition, if the unmodified save roll for an attack made with a missile weapon that targets this model is 6, after all of the attacking unit's attacks have been resolved, you can inflict 1 mortal wound on 1 enemy unit within 9" of this model that is visible to it.

Windleap: *Windmages often accompany Windchargers into battle, allowing the cavalry archers to perform soaring leaps right over the heads of their enemies.*

If a friendly **WINDCHARGERS** unit starts a move wholly within 6" of this model, when it makes that move, that unit has a Move characteristic of 16" and can fly.

MAGIC

This model is a **WIZARD**. It can attempt to cast 1 spell in your hero phase and attempt to unbind 1 spell in the enemy hero phase. It knows the Arcane Bolt, Mystic Shield and Windblast Vortex spells.

Windblast Vortex: *The caster calls forth a vortex that they can send roaring towards the foe at will.*

Windblast Vortex has a casting value of 5. If successfully cast, in your next shooting phase, you can pick 1 enemy unit within 9" of the caster and roll a dice. On a 2+, that enemy unit suffers D3 mortal wounds.

KEYWORDS	ORDER, AELF, LUMINETH REALM-LORDS, AELEMENTIRI, HURAKAN, HERO, WIZARD, WINDMAGE

HURAKAN WINDCHARGERS

	MOVE	
WOUNDS	14"	SAVE
2		5+
	7	
	BRAVERY	

The mounted archers of the Hurakan sprint across the battlefield with the wind at their backs. Their agile Treerunner steeds bound from rock and bough to spring straight past the enemy defences, their riders firing with masterful aim all the while.

MISSILE WEAPONS	Range	Attacks	To Hit	To Wound	Rend	Damage
Windcharger Bow	12"	2	3+	3+	-1	1
MELEE WEAPONS	**Range**	**Attacks**	**To Hit**	**To Wound**	**Rend**	**Damage**
Windcharger Bow	3"	1	3+	3+	-2	1
Claws	1"	2	3+	4+	-	1

DESCRIPTION

A unit of Hurakan Windchargers has any number of models, each armed with a Windcharger Bow.

MOUNT: This unit's Treerunners attack with their Claws.

WINDSPEAKER SENESCHAL: 1 model in this unit can be a Windspeaker Seneschal. Add 1 to the Attacks characteristic of that model's Windcharger Bow.

STANDARD BEARERS: 1 in every 5 models in this unit can be a Standard Bearer. You can re-roll battleshock tests for a unit that includes any Standard Bearers.

ABILITIES

Windcharger Arrows: *Windcharger arrows are guided to their target by aelementor winds.*

Do not apply the cover modifier to save rolls for attacks made with a Windcharger Bow.

Go Where the Wind Blows: *Treerunners can perform seemingly gravity-defying leaps, allowing them to bypass battlefield obstacles with ease.*

When this unit makes a move, it can pass across terrain features in the same manner as a model that can fly.

KEYWORDS	ORDER, AELF, LUMINETH REALM-LORDS, AELEMENTIRI, HURAKAN, WINDCHARGERS

SEVIRETH
LORD OF THE SEVENTH WIND

MOVE **24"**
WOUNDS **10**
SAVE **5+**
BRAVERY **10**

The hot gale of the Hyshian deserts is made manifest in Sevireth. His arrows, though deadly, are not his fiercest weapon, for the sandstorm that whips around him can strip a man's flesh from bone, erode the statues of tyrants, and scour evil men from history.

MISSILE WEAPONS	Range	Attacks	To Hit	To Wound	Rend	Damage
Enathrai, the Howling Death	18"	4	2+	3+	-3	D3
MELEE WEAPONS	Range	Attacks	To Hit	To Wound	Rend	Damage
Enathrai, the Howling Death	3"	2	2+	3+	-2	D3
Swirling Shards	3"	D3	3+	3+	-1	1

DESCRIPTION

Sevireth is a named character that is a single model. He is armed with Enathrai, the Howling Death and Swirling Shards.

FLY: This model can fly.

ABILITIES

Into the Gale: *The cyclonic currents that surround a Spirit of the Wind make it very difficult for enemies to harm them.*

Roll a dice each time you allocate a wound or mortal wound to this model. On a 5+, that wound or mortal wound is negated.

In addition, subtract 2" from the distance enemy models can pile in (to a minimum of 1") while they are within 3" of this model.

Living Cyclone: *As a Spirit of the Wind moves across the battlefield, enemies are picked up and tossed about, buffeted into each other with crushing force by the aelementor's mere passing.*

Roll a dice for each enemy unit that is within 3" of this model after this model makes a charge move. On a 3+, that unit suffers 1 mortal wound, and subtract 1 from hit rolls for that unit until the end of the next combat phase. A unit cannot be affected by this ability more than once per phase.

Scour: *Sevireth has a loathing for the monuments of his enemies, and can use the winds under his control to scour them down to nothing but smooth-surfaced rubble.*

At the start of the charge phase, you can pick 1 faction terrain feature that is within 1" of this model. If you do so, this model cannot charge in that phase but you can roll a dice. On a 2+, the scenery rules on that terrain feature's warscroll cannot be used for the rest of the battle.

Designer's Note: *The terrain feature can still be used to provide cover, and any scenery rules that apply to it which are not on its warscroll can still be used.*

Searing Desert Winds: *Sevireth is lord of burning-hot and parching desert winds. If Sevireth whirls around a foe for long enough, only desiccated corpses are left in his wake.*

After this model makes a normal move (including if it moves at the end of the shooting phase), pick 1 enemy unit that has any models that this model passed across and roll a dice. On a 3+, that unit suffers D3 mortal wounds.

Spirit of the Wind: *A Spirit of the Wind never remains in one place for long.*

At the end of the shooting phase, this model can make a normal move of 12" but cannot run (it can retreat). In addition, this model can retreat and still charge later in the same turn.

Windmage Symbiosis: *Windmages are able to sustain Spirits of the Wind, refreshing the elemental energies that are their life force.*

In your hero phase, if this model is within 12" of any friendly **WINDMAGES**, you can heal up to D3 wounds allocated to this model.

KEYWORDS	ORDER, LUMINETH REALM-LORDS, HURAKAN, YMETRICA, HERO, SPIRIT OF THE WIND, SEVIRETH

HURAKAN SPIRIT OF THE WIND

MOVE 24"

WOUNDS 8

SAVE 5+

BRAVERY 10

The winds of Hysh were forced to watch as the lands they once loved were corrupted by Chaos. Now, given focus by the Lumineth, they take the fight to the hated agents of disorder with arcane arrow, swirling shard-storm, and raging vortex all at once.

MISSILE WEAPONS	Range	Attacks	To Hit	To Wound	Rend	Damage
Bow of the Wind's Vengeance	18"	4	2+	3+	-2	D3
MELEE WEAPONS	Range	Attacks	To Hit	To Wound	Rend	Damage
Bow of the Wind's Vengeance	3"	2	2+	3+	-2	D3
Swirling Shards	3"	D3	3+	3+	-1	1

DESCRIPTION

A Hurakan Spirit of the Wind is a single model armed with a Bow of the Wind's Vengeance and Swirling Shards.

FLY: This model can fly.

ABILITIES

Into the Gale: *The cyclonic currents that surround a Spirit of the Wind make it very difficult for enemies to harm them.*

Roll a dice each time you allocate a wound or mortal wound to this model. On a 5+, that wound or mortal wound is negated.

In addition, subtract 2" from the distance enemy models can pile in (to a minimum of 1") while they are within 3" of this model.

Living Cyclone: *As a Spirit of the Wind moves across the battlefield, enemies are picked up and tossed about, buffeted into each other with crushing force by the aelementor's mere passing.*

Roll a dice for each enemy unit that is within 3" of this model after this model makes a charge move. On a 3+, that unit suffers 1 mortal wound, and subtract 1 from hit rolls for that unit until the end of the next combat phase. A unit cannot be affected by this ability more than once per phase.

Spirit of the Wind: *A Spirit of the Wind never remains in one place for long.*

At the end of the shooting phase, this model can make a normal move of 12" but cannot run (it can retreat). In addition, this model can retreat and still charge later in the same turn.

Windmage Symbiosis: *Windmages are able to sustain Spirits of the Wind, refreshing the elemental energies that are their life force.*

In your hero phase, if this model is within 12" of any friendly **WINDMAGES**, you can heal up to D3 wounds allocated to this model.

KEYWORDS	ORDER, LUMINETH REALM-LORDS, HURAKAN, SPIRIT OF THE WIND

MYARI LIGHTCALLER

MOVE 6"
WOUNDS 5
SAVE 5+
BRAVERY 8

Steeped in arcane skill, Myari Lightcaller leads a tight-knit group of Lumineth in an attempt to stop the Katophrane curse from spreading across the Mortal Realms. Bolstered by his familiar Ulari, he wields Hyshian magic to dazzle and sear his foes.

MISSILE WEAPONS	Range	Attacks	To Hit	To Wound	Rend	Damage
Searing Beams	18"	3	3+	3+	-2	1
MELEE WEAPONS	Range	Attacks	To Hit	To Wound	Rend	Damage
Staff of Enlightenment	1"	3	3+	3+	-1	D3

DESCRIPTION

Myari Lightcaller is a named character that is a single model. He is armed with Searing Beams and the Staff of Enlightenment.

ABILITIES

Scryowl Familiar: *Nothing escapes the piercing gaze of Myari's familiar, Ulari, as the scryowl soars above the battlefield.*

Add 1 to casting, unbinding and dispelling rolls for this model. In addition, at the start of your

hero phase and at the start of your shooting phase, you can pick 1 enemy unit within 24" of this model that is not visible to this model. That enemy unit is visible to this model until the end of that phase.

MAGIC

This model is a **WIZARD**. It can attempt to cast 1 spell in your hero phase and attempt to unbind 1 spell in the enemy hero phase. It knows the Arcane Bolt, Mystic Shield and Dazzling Light spells.

Dazzling Light: *The caster surrounds themselves and nearby allies with blinding light, forcing foes to avert their gaze.*

Dazzling Light has a casting value of 6. If successfully cast, until your next hero phase, subtract 1 from hit rolls for attacks that target the caster and subtract 1 from hit rolls for attacks made with missile weapons that target other friendly units wholly within 6" of the caster.

KEYWORDS	ORDER, AELF, LUMINETH REALM-LORDS, SCINARI, YMETRICA, HERO, WIZARD, MYARI LIGHTCALLER

MYARI'S PURIFIERS

MOVE 6"
WOUNDS 2
SAVE 4+
BRAVERY 7

Myari's Purifiers epitomise different aspects of the Lumineth way of war. Bahannar cleaves to the Alarith tradition, whilst Senaela is an expert archer and Ailenn, as a Bladelord, has a near-supernatural mastery over the arts of the sword.

MISSILE WEAPONS	Range	Attacks	To Hit	To Wound	Rend	Damage
Auralan Bow	18"	2	3+	4+	-1	1
MELEE WEAPONS	Range	Attacks	To Hit	To Wound	Rend	Damage
Stone Mallet	1"	3	3+	3+	-1	1
Sunmetal Greatsword	1"	2	2+	2+	-1	1
Vanari Dagger	1"	1	3+	4+	-	1

DESCRIPTION

Myari's Purifiers is a unit that has 3 models. Ailenn, the Mind's Edge, is armed with a Sunmetal Greatsword; Bahannar is armed with a Stone Mallet; and Senaela is armed with an Auralan Bow and Vanari Dagger.

ABILITIES

Crushing Blow: *The Stoneguard land blows with the power of a mountain avalanche.*

If the unmodified hit roll for an attack made with this unit's Stone Mallet is 6, add 1 to the damage inflicted if that attack is successful.

Guardians: *The Purifiers fight alongside Myari Lightcaller, protecting the mage from harm.*

Roll a dice before you allocate a wound or mortal wound to a friendly **MYARI LIGHTCALLER** within 3" of this unit. On a 2+, you must allocate that wound or mortal wound to this unit instead.

Sunmetal Weapons: *Weapons forged from sunmetal can burn a victim from the inside out.*

If the unmodified hit roll for an attack made with this unit's Sunmetal Greatsword or Auralan Bow is 6, that attack inflicts 1 mortal wound on the target and the attack sequence ends (do not make a wound or save roll).

KEYWORDS	ORDER, AELF, LUMINETH REALM-LORDS, YMETRICA, MYARI'S PURIFIERS

PITCHED BATTLE PROFILES

The table below provides points, minimum and maximum unit sizes and battlefield roles for the warscrolls and warscroll battalions in this book, for use in Pitched Battles. Spending the points listed on these tables allows you to take a minimum-sized unit with any of its upgrades. Understrength units cost the full amount of points. Larger units are taken in multiples of their minimum unit size; multiply their cost by the same amount as you multiplied their size. If a unit has two points values separated by a slash (e.g. '60/200'), the second value is for a maximum-sized unit. 'Unique' units are named characters and can only be taken once in an army. Updated March 2021; the profiles printed here take precedence over any profiles with an earlier publication date or no publication date.

CITIES OF SIGMAR WARSCROLL	UNIT SIZE MIN	MAX	POINTS	BATTLEFIELD ROLE	NOTES
Xintil War-magi	-	-	140	*Warscroll Battalion*	

FLESH-EATER COURTS WARSCROLL	UNIT SIZE MIN	MAX	POINTS	BATTLEFIELD ROLE	NOTES
Mortevell's Helcourt	-	-	100	*Warscroll Battalion*	

LUMINETH REALM-LORDS WARSCROLL	UNIT SIZE MIN	MAX	POINTS	BATTLEFIELD ROLE	NOTES
Vanari Starshard Ballistas	1	1	100	Artillery	
Ellania and Ellathor, Eclipsian Warsages	1	1	260	Leader	Unique. This model can be included as an ally in any army that has an **ORDER** general.
Hurakan Windmage	1	1	120	Leader	
Lyrior Uthralle	1	1	210	Leader	Unique
Scinari Calligrave	1	1	100	Leader	
Scinari Loreseeker	1	1	160	Leader	Unique
Sevireth, Lord of the Seventh Wind	1	1	300	Leader	Unique
Vanari Bannerblade	1	1	110	Leader	
Vanari Lord Regent	1	1	150	Leader	
Hurakan Spirit of the Wind	1	1	250		
Hurakan Windchargers	5	15	130		Battleline in a **HELON** army
Vanari Bladelords	5	15	120		For each **SCINARI HERO** included in your army, you can take 1 Vanari Bladelords unit as a Battleline unit.
Myari Lightcaller	1	1	220	Leader	Unique. These units must be taken as a set for a total of 220 points. Although taken as a set, each is a separate unit.
Myari's Purifiers	3	3			
Bladelord Host	-	-	100	*Warscroll Battalion*	
Hurakan Temple	-	-	180	*Warscroll Battalion*	
Lumineth Battlehost	-	-	50	*Warscroll Battalion*	
Starshard Battery	-	-	120	*Warscroll Battalion*	
Shrine Luminor	1	1	0	*Scenery*	

OSSIARCH BONEREAPERS WARSCROLL	UNIT SIZE MIN	MAX	POINTS	BATTLEFIELD ROLE	NOTES
Horrek's Dreadlance	-	-	120	*Warscroll Battalion*	

NURGLE WARSCROLL	UNIT SIZE MIN	MAX	POINTS	BATTLEFIELD ROLE	NOTES
Sloppity Bilepiper, Herald of Nurgle	1	1	150	Leader	
Spoilpox Scrivener, Herald of Nurgle	1	1	140	Leader	
Beasts of Nurgle	1	3	120		
Invidian Plaguehost	-	-	120	*Warscroll Battalion*